CLEARLY SEEN

Constructing Solid Arguments for Design

RANDY J. GULIUZZA

INSTITUTE FOR CREATION RESEARCH

Dallas, TX | www.icr.org

Dr. Randy Guliuzza is a captivating speaker who presents well-documented and often humorous scientific and biblical talks to audiences of all ages. He has represented ICR in several scientific debates at secular universities and in other forums. Dr. Guliuzza has a B.S. in Engineering from the South Dakota School of Mines and Technology, a B.A. in theology from Moody Bible Institute, an M.D. from the University of Minnesota, and a Masters in Public Health from Harvard University. Dr. Guliuzza served nine years in the Navy Civil Engineer Corps and is a registered Professional Engineer. In 2008, he retired as Lt. Col. from the U.S. Air Force, where he served as Flight Surgeon and Chief of Aerospace Medicine. He is the author of *Made in His Image: Examining the complexities of the human body.*

CLEARLY SEEN

Constructing Solid Arguments For Design

BY RANDY J. GULIUZZA, P.E., M.D.

First printing: November 2012

All Scripture quotations are from the King James Version.

ISBN: 978-1-935587-13-2
Library of Congress Catalog Number: 2012945061

Please visit our website for other books and resources: www.icr.org.

Printed in the United States of America.

TABLE OF CONTENTS

FOREWORD

Known unto God are all his works from the beginning of the world.

Acts 15:18

Even those with only a passing knowledge of the Bible's message would recognize that the God of Scripture is not an arbitrary, purposeless, disinterested, disconnected deity drifting around somewhere out there" in space. The essence of the Christian gospel is that God is personally interested in His creation and that He planned the work necessary for our salvation "from the foundation of the world" (Revelation 13:8).

Logic alone would dictate that we should therefore expect design and order, purpose and meaning in everything that surrounds us. Even Job's theologically confused friends knew that anyone could "ask now the beasts, and they shall teach thee; and the fowls of the air, and they shall tell thee….Who knoweth not in all these that the hand of the LORD hath wrought this? In whose hand is the soul of every living thing, and the breath of all mankind. Doth not the ear try words? and the mouth taste his meat?" (Job 12:7-11).

The evidence for God's design is as obvious as sound and taste.

No wonder the psalmist eagerly proclaimed, "The heavens declare the glory of God; and the firmament sheweth his handywork. Day unto day uttereth speech, and night unto night sheweth knowledge. There is no speech nor language, where their voice is not heard. Their line is gone out through all the earth, and their words to the end of the world" (Psalm 19:1-4). The whole universe, from the jaw-dropping majesty of the galaxies to the curiously exciting inner workings of the cell, continually broadcasts the evidence for God's handiwork.

Yet in spite of this overwhelming evidence—evidence that is in every nook and cranny of our universe—evolutionary dogma declares that the evidence of design and purpose is only "apparent" and that everything we see came about through random chance. Evolutionists claim that it looks like a duck, and quacks like a duck, and moves like a duck, but it most certainly is not a duck! One wonders how people with a pedigree education can hold a straight face when they tell such tales.

Dr. Randy Guliuzza has several of those pedigree degrees. He has an undergraduate degree in engineering from the South Dakota School of Mines and Technology, a B.A. in theology from Moody Bible Institute, an M.D. from the University of Minnesota, and a Masters in Public Health from Harvard University, and he insists that the design of everything in the universe is *clearly seen*!

Evidence—scientific evidence, empirical evidence—is everywhere observable and testable. There is no confusion. There are no difficult and mysterious processes that can only be understood by people with Ph.D.'s. Even God's invisible attributes are "clearly seen, being understood by the things that are made, even his eternal power and Godhead; so that they [those who deny God and His work] are without excuse" (Romans 1:20).

Clearly Seen is a wonderful book, full of inescapable examples of God's design. Not only are there delightful and understandable illustrations of the evidence for design, but also clear indictments of the false logic and deceptive language that naturalistic philosophers use to obfuscate the obvious. It even includes a special study section to reinforce its solid arguments for the design and purpose God built into His world.

Whether used by homeschool teachers, in small group meetings, or for personal study, *Clearly Seen* will give believers confidence that what the Creator says about His creation is true, as well as equip them with the tools they need to demonstrate to others that the design they clearly see in nature was, in fact, put there by a Master Designer whom they can also know as their Savior.

Henry M. Morris III
Chief Executive Officer
Institute for Creation Research

INTRODUCTION

This is possibly the first creation book devoted to training Christians on the best methods to explain intelligent design. As such, it is meant to be of practical use, providing a step-by-step teaching guide for using the living things that the Lord Jesus has made as a witness to His reality, while capably unwrapping their astounding designs as a witness for His engineering genius.

Though a lot of science is discussed, the book is grounded on the biblical truth that the design in created things is clearly seen by everyone. Romans 1:19-20 states, "Because that which may be known of God is manifest in them; for God has [*shown*] it unto them. For the invisible things of him from the *creation* of the world are clearly seen, being understood by the things that are *made*" (emphasis added). It is telling that the key words in these verses are related to design as the sign for all to see.

This book will help Christians detail for others how design is the best explanation for the observable evidence. There are many things people see and intuitively know, but find hard to put into words. *Clearly Seen: Constructing Solid Arguments for Design* shows Christians how to package those insights by demonstrating how to apply straightforward, day-to-day concepts of design to the world around us—especially in the sections titled "Learning a Short Example" and "Pulling It

All Together." Also included is a final chapter summarizing the importance of the creation account to our understanding of who God is, as well as study questions and answers for use in classrooms, small groups, and personal study.

Anybody in any culture at any time in history has watched something being created (fashioned, made) by a creator and knows that things don't create themselves. The same distinctive design features in human-designed things are clearly seen in humans and other organisms; thus, they too must have had a Creator. So, acknowledging the real design seen in living things is the first step for people to both know their Creator and to think correctly about His creation—*design-centered thinking* is fundamental to starting down the correct path to understanding living things.

I would like to thank the editorial staff at ICR who contributed to making this book possible, but especially Beth Mull whose expertise should be recognized for improving all of the materials. A big "thank you" belongs to my wife, June, who not only patiently—and constructively—listened to all of my (sometimes animated) oral deliberations before and during writing, but also reviewed all of the articles for this book and my prior book, *Made in His Image: Examining the complexities of the human body*, also published by the Institute for Creation Research.

FIT & FUNCTION:
Design in Nature

To help others understand that Christ is their Creator, use the approach the Bible says *always* provokes a living conscience: "For the invisible things of him from the creation of the world are clearly seen, being understood by the things that are made" (Romans 1:20). Simply using humanity's natural tendency to deduce the fact that complex design requires a designer is more powerful in showing the handiwork of Christ than evidence from fossils or genetics—and it's easier.

It's no surprise that psychological research shows that creation-based thinking comes naturally, while evolutionary thinking is not natural. This is an integral trait of every human—and it is *never* going away. When believers see the underlying attributes of design, they can communicate that to others to help them understand that what they see in nature was, in fact, designed.

Discussing Design Naturally Connects with People

Begin by using the word *purpose*—which definitively captures the very essence of design—early and often. This word is also an ideal bridge to human inquisitiveness. Given an object, people naturally reason *first* about how it works and its intended function. Research shows that humans are naturally compelled to seek explanations of purpose, with "pleasure" areas in the brain being rewarded when it is discovered, but are left feeling frustrated when explanations are elusive. The process of discovering purpose is captivating and emotionally stimulating, similar to the experience of unwrapping a present.

Also, people intuitively link purpose with intelligence. This predisposition is *not* culturally or religiously transmitted, but appears to be instinctive.[1] If asked where an animal came from, young children—in all cultures—naturally say, in essence, "God made it."

The engineering and legal professions have formally recognized the concept that human insight sensibly links purpose and design in everyday life. According to the Accreditation Board for Engineering and Technology definition for design, "Engineering design is the process of devising a system, component, or process to meet desired needs."[2] Societies rely on the legal consequences of purposeful intent to guarantee performance. Precise language is commonly included in construction contracts—specifically, to obtain from contractors a final product that satisfies a purpose. This is so crucial that even if a contract lacks a precise statement of performance, courts during a dispute usually imply a purpose that legally deems a project complete when it functions "fit for its intended purpose."

What is superior about nature is that people can be challenged to look around at leaves, grass, feathers, fur—indeed *anything*—and see whether it fulfills its purpose(s). It is like the Lord has given a humanly unparalleled performance guarantee that whatever He builds is *always* suitable for its purpose.

After establishing the basic concept of purpose, couple it to the word *fit*. People easily see when things match or complement each other. When things fit (a principle at the heart of design), a clear-cut mental impression is made: Humans perceive that when things are a perfect fit, they were meant to work together.

Fit can be pointed out everywhere. Creatures are superbly fit to their specific environments (such as fish in their water world), but their body parts also fit precisely, and even the structures of their molecules fit just right. Therefore, reinforce what studies already show: People resist, by nature and experience, explaining great fit—especially by random chance—with anything other than great design. Using the words *purpose* and *fit* is like pushing the buttons corresponding to *design* in people's minds.

Be Confident That Everybody Comprehends Design in Nature

Some evolutionary psychoanalysts assert

that people are naturally constrained with a "very specific cognitive glitch" when it comes to understanding their origins. They find this "puzzling"[1] and some get "angry"[3] that more Americans believe in angels than in evolution. The real reason for this "glitch" is simple. Everywhere that people—even ardent evolutionists—look, nature teems with complex creatures that clearly appear to have been designed.

In 1859 in a section of his book *The Origin of Species* entitled "Organs of Extreme Perfection and Complication," Charles Darwin recognized that nature appeared to have been designed. Little had changed by 1971, when French biologist and Nobel winner Jacques Monod commented on what alien beings (via a computer on earth) would observe by merely studying a colony of bees:

> The extreme complexity of their structure…is reproduced with extraordinary fidelity from one individual bee to the next. Powerful evidence, is it not, that these creatures are the products of a deliberate, constructive, and highly sophisticated order of activity?[4]

Richard Lewontin, the Alexander Agassiz Research Professor at Harvard, once eloquently said:

> Life forms are more than simply multiple and diverse, however. Organisms fit remarkably well into the external world in which they live. They have morphologies, physiologies and behaviors that appear to have been carefully and artfully designed to enable each organism to appropriate the world around it for its own life.[5]

Even today's most vocal evolutionist, Richard Dawkins, affirmed that "biology is the study of complicated things that have the appearance of having been designed for a purpose."[6] It is vitally important to understand, however, that Lewontin and Dawkins used the word "appear" quite literally to mean that things only *seem like* or *look as if* they are designed, giving the *illusion* of a real designer.

Suddenly, the real issue becomes crystal clear—namely, not whether design actually exists, but what the *best explanation* is for the

origin of fit, function, and design. Either the design flows from a real designer and is genuine design—the naturally favored reason—or there is no designer and the "apparent" design everyone clearly sees is all a false impression, which is a tough sell for evolutionists.

Learning a Short Example

Consider making this point by using something like the three precisely shaped bones in the human middle ear.[7] Suspended by thread-like ligaments, these span the space from the eardrum to the sound-sensing organ called the cochlea. They fit together seamlessly, connected with tiny lubricant-filled joint capsules that enable interactions sensitive enough to detect sound vibrations from 20 to 20,000 times per second.

> Psychological research shows that creation-based thinking comes naturally, while evolutionary thinking is not natural.

Sound intensities can be heard from a pin drop to more than 10 million times as intense, in part because these bony interactions allow sound waves collected in the *air* by the eardrum to be amplified 20 times—which matches exactly with sound transmission properties of the *fluid* in the cochlea. Yet in response to loud noises, the bone's efficient vibratory interactions can be damped in a split second by two very small attached muscles that reflexively contract, thus protecting the bones and cochlea from damage.

Evolutionists claim that these bones' fit and function only *appear* to be the work of a real designer. They earnestly contend that during reptilian evolution, two bones involved with the hinge-jaw of certain reptiles migrated (while changing shape) from the jaw to the middle ear and connected to an existing bone, thus becoming the three inner ear bones of mammals.[8] Creationists maintain that a real

designer is a better explanation for the exquisite design of human middle ear bones.

Pulling It All Together

Elite scientific culture is *not* popular culture, so the mental process of most people, Christian and non-Christian, still functions normally in attributing design to a designer.[1] This is true in any society, particularly with young people. Conversations can be readily started, for example, by saying, "I read something about how the three tiny bones in your ear confer great capabilities for hearing." Be sure to include enough details describing precise *fit* and *purpose* to highlight design and to keep the topic interesting. Most people will listen since: 1) once engaged, people have an almost irresistible urge to know how and why things work; and 2) there is an emotional thrill tied to "discovery"—particularly if the brain is tantalized as information unfolds bit-by-bit.

The main issue is the best explanation for the design apparent in nature. Be prepared to explain the standard evolutionary story if asked, but clearly state that after examining alternative explanations, you remain persuaded that the best reason for design is a real designer—a conclusion consistent with everything humans know intuitively and by experience.

Perhaps someone may be ready to know that Designer, the Lord Jesus Christ, and by knowing Him enter into eternal life (John 17:3). This is not exploiting a "cognitive glitch" of humans, but using the witness of design that the Lord has provided. The things the Lord has made are so astounding that He's made it easy for people to see Him as their Creator, and hard—to the point of suppressing what is obvious—to deny Him. ●

References
1. Bering, J. Creationism Feels Right, but That Doesn't Make it So. *Scientific American*, posted on sciam.com March 19, 2009, accessed March 19, 2009.
2. ABET Definition of Design. The University of Nevada, Las Vegas. Posted on me.unlv.edu, accessed December 1, 2009.
3. Dawkins, R. The Angry Evolutionist. *Newsweek*. Posted on newsweek.com September 25, 2009, accessed December 1, 2009.
4. Monod, J. 1971. *Chance and Necessity: An Essay on the Natural Philosophy of Modern Biology*. New York: Alfred A. Knopf, 7.
5. Lewontin, R. C. 1978. Adaptation. *Scientific American*. 239: 213.
6. Dawkins, R. 1986. *The Blind Watchmaker*. London: W. W. Norton & Company, 1.
7. For a book of examples, see Guliuzza, R. 2009. *Made in His Image*. Dallas, TX: Institute for Creation Research.
8. Gilbert, S. F. 2006. *Developmental Biology*, 8th ed. Sunderland, MA: Sinauer Associates, 17 and 742.

Unmasking Evolution's Magic Words

Everyone certainly sees design in nature by observing the purpose of precisely fitted parts—those in fish gills or bird wings, for instance, enable those animals to fit into their environments. Evolutionists, however, seek to suppress humans' natural tendency to link features of design to a real designer. They teach that complex animals only *appear* to be designed and that what looks like intelligent crafting is only an illusion.

Why not accept that evolutionary explanation? This is a fair question, but there is no need to jump right into a list of scientific problems raised by evolution. Instead, start with what is relevant to explaining design: the fact that evolutionary "science" is *different* from sciences that use natural, repeatable, and verifiable methods to explain phenomena. Evolution is fundamentally a historical narrative—a story—that attempts to reconstruct unseen past events.[1] Many people find this story too weak to be a persuasive reason for design, since it is built on absolute chance and uses remarkably unscientific language within its explanations.

Evolutionists Explain Design Using Unscientific "Magic Words"

The term "magic words" is used here as a concise idiom that describes the *best* words evolutionists use to explain "apparent" design. Evolutionists confidently insist that a complex biological feature simply "appeared," "emerged," "arose," "gave rise to," "burst onto the scene," "evolved itself," "derived," "was on the way to becoming," "radiated into," "modified itself," "became a miracle of evolution," "was making the transition to," "manufactured itself," "evolution's way of dealing with," "derived emergent properties," or "was lucky."

How do words like "appeared" explain design? Just like magic, the use of this word invokes mysterious powers within unseen universes that are capable of leaping over enormous scientific obstacles without having to provide any scientific consideration for how a particular physical result was achieved. Magic words convey wish-like convictions that if evolutionists just believe deeply enough, their explanations *must* be true and someday *will* be true—though currently resisted by all scientific evidence. Explaining design by believing it "arose" appeals to imaginary special forces which help evolutionists to connect the evolutionary dots. But as in any magical kingdom, the connections are mental fantasies that are not grounded in reality.

Magic words lack explanatory power because they fail to tie real observations to detailed descriptions of *how* features of design originate. Claiming that novel biological features "burst onto the scene" abandons the need for experimental verification; indeed, the implication is to not even try. Take any biological *observation*. In evolutionary thinking, any observation can be transformed into a proof that explains its own existence by applying the magic phrase: "It *exists* because it is favored by natural selection." In reality, observations are only observations and are neither proofs nor explanations.

Engineers, medical doctors, and other scientists who rely on studies or experiments do not use these kinds of words. Their products do not "emerge" but develop via thought-filled processes. They rightly call filling a knowledge gap with narrative stories "arm waving," which calls to mind a stage magician.

In conversation with others, it would be difficult to overemphasize how important magic words are to evolutionary theory. Remark on how these words pervade elite journals like *Science*, popular magazines like *Scientific American*, and television shows like *NOVA*. "Magic words" pour from evolutionary literature like water over Niagara Falls. Challenge your listener to carefully observe the communication in these forums, noting how many paragraphs or statements pass without the use of these words. They are the lifeblood of the evolutionary community's most profound and highest-quality scientific literature.

Evolutionists Insist Chance Alone Produces Design

People should be educated about the central—but cleverly de-emphasized—dogma of evolution, that complex design is a wholly *chance* outcome of natural processes operating in a mindless, self-contained system that does not determine need or purpose in advance, and sets no direction. Distinguished science historian Jacques Barzun described the key elements of evolution as "the sum total of the accidents of life acting upon the sum total of the accidents of variation" leading to a "completely mechanistic and material system"[2]—i.e., one with no God.

In 1995, the influential National Association of Biology Teachers crafted a definitive "Statement on the Teaching of Evolution" that affirmed the centrality of chance. Their first tenet read, "The diversity of life on Earth is the outcome of evolution: an unsupervised, impersonal, unpredictable and natural process of temporal descent with genetic modification that is affected by natural selection, chance, historical contingencies and changing environments."[3]

Newsweek summed up the view of Harvard's renowned paleontologist Stephen Jay Gould:

Why did some lineages survive while most perished? There is no obvious reason, says Gould. The survivors were not simpler or more complex, more generalized or specialized, more numerous or superior in any obvious way;...The obvious answer, but one which most people instinctively resist, is that they were lucky.[4]

Not only is there instinctive resistance to this answer, but it is intellectually distasteful to credit blind luck for complex designs. People experientially know designers are—without exception—the real cause. Teachers of evolution, therefore, do not attempt to get people to swallow in one big gulp a single colossal chance explanation. Instead, they adroitly assert that what *seems like* a huge chance biological event is simply the cumulative effect of *countless tiny lucky events* arising over enormous time periods in primitive life forms' descendants. People relate readily to coincidental, almost happenstance, events. If these are coupled to staggeringly long timescales, biological wonders that are intuitively impossible...well, might just happen.

To counteract this thinking, offer a dose of reality. Point out that scientists never actually *observe* random DNA mistakes accumu-

lating to generate from scratch the instructions necessary to build the type of complexity seen in biological structures.

Learning a Short Example

Do major science journals overcome barriers to evolution by using jargon and magical concepts to hurdle them in a single bound? Yes, as typified in the *Archives of Ophthalmology*'s account for the origin of the eye lens:

Lenses in different species may originate from different tissues in the embryo. But no matter what the source tissue, the substance that makes up the lens body must show a graded difference in density: greater in the center with a resulting higher index of refraction, less dense in the periphery with a lower index of refraction. This has been evolution's way of dealing with spherical aberration, a particularly pressing problem.[5]

> Magic words convey wish-like convictions that if evolutionists just believe deeply enough, their explanations *must* be true and someday *will* be true.

How *did* evolution deal with it? The "complex genetic programs were lying in wait" to build all eye structures, including the lens proteins which were "recruited" via "molecular opportunism" to perform *totally new functions* since "evolution uses what is available. It is a consummate recycler."[5] Really?

The graded density of lens proteins—a great design feature—overcomes spherical aberration by allowing light entering through *any spot* of the lens to focus to a clear point (good vision) rather than many points (poor vision). Evolutionists should also consider that lens proteins just happen to be shaped and arranged to allow the lens to change profile to focus images from near or far—provided it is suspended precisely behind the pupil by hundreds of surrounding ligaments attached on one end to a special lens capsule and the other end to a circular muscle anchored to the reti-

na. Indeed, *hundreds* of other design features could be listed which are better explained as resulting from a real designer.

Pulling It All Together

A quick response to a question of why evolution is not a satisfactory explanation for design might be:

I've been less than persuaded by what I was taught in school and on educational programs. Leading evolutionists insist that the mutational mechanism of evolution is random with respect to any goal. I have never observed a process driven by chance which absolutely excludes intelligent oversight to produce features of design. From what I read and see on TV, evolutionists jump over details by using magical words like "arose," "appeared," "gave rise to," and "evolved itself" to explain how chance produces design. Even the *leading* journal for eye doctors recently used those words to describe eye evolution. The engineering feats I see are always the result of real designers, so I enjoy being free from the need to rely on the vague, non-scientific words evolutionists use.

This illustrates why evolution, as only a historical narrative, is different from other types of science that use real experiments. I find it hard to substitute stories for direct observations. I also enjoy freedom from being forced to call design "an illusion'"—a poor reason—simply because it excludes divine intervention.

By helping people understand the *best explanation* for the *origin* of design, they can be influenced to see Christ as their Creator, just as the Bible says: "For the invisible things of him from the creation of the world are clearly seen, being understood by the things that are made" (Romans 1:20). ●

References
1. Mayr, E. Darwin's Influence on Modern Thought. *Scientific American.* July 2000, 80.
2. Barzun, J.1981. *Darwin, Marx, Wagner: Critique of a Heritage,* 2nd ed. Chicago: University of Chicago Press, 11 and 36.
3. NABT Unveils New Statement on Teaching Evolution. *The American Biology Teacher.* January 1996, 58 (1): 61-2. Since then, "unsupervised" and "impersonal" have been removed. The 2008 statement is so evolutionarily neutered that creationists could concur with many tenets.
4. Adler, J. We're All Lucky to Be Here. *Newsweek,* November 20, 1989, 68.
5. Fishman, R. S. 2008. Evolution and the Eye. *Archives of Ophthalmology.* 126 (11): 1586-1592.

Natural Selection Is Not "Nature's Design Process"

The popular documentary series *Skyscraper* featured a fascinating look at architects using the design process. Viewers appreciated learning how this process is implemented. For anyone wanting to create the *best explanation* for the origin of nature's design—which is the main issue—learning this process is vital. Charles Darwin faced an extraordinarily difficult task in devising his naturalistic explanation. He needed to find a *source* of intelligence—a substitute god—to explain *how* the diversity of life could display countless features that clearly look like they were chosen by intelligence for specific purposes. His clever explanation? Natural selection.

After 150 years, natural selection stands as the only credible alternative to supernatural creation. But showing someone why Darwin's concept cannot explain anything about the origin of complex design requires an understanding of why the words "selection" and "natural" are so widely influential.

Making Natural Selection Look Like Human Engineering

Consider why intelligence is naturally coupled to design. First, engineers use a process that *sees* a need. Next, they develop a plan that depends heavily on *selecting* the best parts and processes that *fit* specific characteristics of the need. A special *decision-making* capacity, called intelligence, is vital to "see" and "select." Everyone can discern that intelligence is *only* found in certain living things, primarily humans and God.

The word "select" becomes the key to understanding Darwin's link between the intelligent living world and non-thinking nature. His stroke of genius for those who reject supernatural origins was to take the random phenomena of whether the traits of living things either fit their environment or not and then call it a "selection" process of "nature." From this he extrapolated the idea that nature could make *choices*, which then allowed the plausible conclusion that nature actually possesses a sort of innate *intelligence*. Thus, Darwin successfully injected the attribute of intelligence into the non-living world—a feat many thought impossible. How did he advance this counterintuitive concept?

Darwin began *Origin of Species* with the simple observation that offspring are very similar to their parents, but not exactly the same. Differences between parent and offspring (or between siblings) were important because nature might favor—"select"—those that afforded better chances for survival. If differences accumulate over time, then future offspring may be very different from their ancestors—a truly elegant and simple, yet reasonable, observation that creatively promoted a type of intelligence in nature. And not just a simple intelligence: nature is portrayed as somehow *thinking*—a talented stand-in god—that always chooses the "best" traits and "saves" them to "build" things.

The power of this concept to captivate minds must never be underestimated. It is taught in most schools as absolutely true. Understanding this provides a thoughtful way to turn a conversation by saying, "Darwin had the most incredible idea ever conceived to explain design naturally. But, like all ideas, his was not perfect— it really does not *explain* design."

"But why can't it explain design?" Natural selection can be seen as an *observation* about genetic variants that allow differences in survival. But when used to *explain* the origin of a design, it becomes a crippled explanation, making great claims that it cannot support. Why? Because the "selection" it portrays is a distortion of selection in real design processes.

Unintelligent Nature Fails as a Design Process

In design processes, engineers bear the burden to do what only they are able to do—choose elements for their plan that best fit the characteristics for meeting the need. A plan that fits the characteristics "survives" the process. The engineers are active and the need is passive. Process cannot be viewed from the perspective of the "need"—that it "selected" vital features of the plan. Intelligence would then be attributed to a non-living thing, which does not take place in human design processes. Yet, this is precisely what Darwin does with natural selection—nature's so-called design process. This lends to the "conclusion that these favored individuals had been selected to survive," as Harvard's foremost evolutionist, Ernst Mayr, wrote.[1] But nature does not have decision-making intelligence.

In nature, *living* organisms must do what *only* they can do. They must generate the diversity of traits—via a "selection" process within their own DNA—that will fit vital characteristics to live within their environments. If no

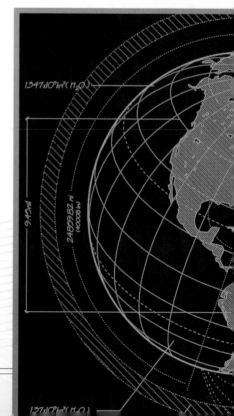

members of a group generate suitable traits, the group goes extinct. If some members generate traits that fit, they survive. Information within DNA and how that information is expressed correspond to the thinking and selecting of a real engineer. Living organisms are active, environments are passive.

Darwin's theory misrepresents the design process, viewing it mostly from the perspective of a passive environment that is falsely empowered to "select" the best traits. This masquerade was well-illustrated by Mayr: "A process of selection would have a concrete objective, the determination of the 'best' or 'fittest' phenotype."[2] But in reality, the environment (or "nature") never selects or sets "concrete objectives."

Whether creatures live or die depends on *their* ability to generate information from *their* DNA[3] to produce specific traits that fit environments. Thus, the ability to generate "beneficial variations"[4] *already resides* in the living organism. This is the source of design that natural selection fails to explain. The theory fraudulently ascribes the powers of diversification to variables outside the creature when diversity depends solely on variables inside the creature.

Darwin's Theory Uses Circular Reasoning

Genetic variants may cause differences in survival, but that has nothing to do with *explaining* their design. What requires explanation is the origin of the biological apparatus with the ability to generate, save, and pass on variations in the first place.

On this point, Darwin's theory provides no useful knowledge, claiming, "nature's designer is nature"—an intrinsically circular explanation. It becomes undeniable since "cause" and "effect" are seen as equivalent. Not a single advocate of evolution can escape this circular reasoning. For them, the widespread circular reasoning that "it exists because it is favored by natural selection" is very compelling, but can be countered by showing that their influence resides more in the force of *decree* than in the power of explanation.

> Natural selection is at best an observation about genetic variants and differences in survival. As an explanation of design, it is completely crippled.

Attributing design to "natural selection" is also circular—but at a deeper level—making it harder to spot. Here is the circular part: "nature" is said to encompass both the environment *and living things.* Thus, the intelligent information residing in living things—the true source of design—is assimilated into "nature" and then cleverly credited to it. The step-by-step explanation for its origin is *completely disregarded.* So, "nature" has self-evident powers to "select" and save its own genetic varieties. As one evolutionist said, "Its truth is apparent" with "enormous power" as "a weapon of explanation."[5] However, this "weapon" only shoots blanks, since Darwin's great explanation merely *explains itself*—a basic "truth" for evolution, but something wholly unacceptable to science.

Learning a Short Example

Look closely at Ernst Mayr's defense of Darwin for accepting that natural selection is nothing but "survival of the fittest":

> Darwin adopted Spencer's metaphor in his later work. However, his opponents claimed that it was…a circular statement by defining "the fittest" as those who survive, but this is a misleading claim. Actually, survival is not a property of an organism but only an indication of the existence of certain survival-favoring attributes.[6]

Mayr's circular analysis is evident even as he denies that Darwinism is circular. According to him, "an indication of the existence of certain survival-favoring attributes" is…"survival." He cannot escape circular thinking.

Pulling It All Together

Only two explanations remain for the origin of nature's design: supernatural intelligence or natural selection. Evolutionists claim that the real design clearly seen in nature is only an appearance, while the apparent decision-making intelligence in nature is real. Both assertions are wrong.

Natural selection is at best an observation about genetic variants and differences in survival. As an explanation of design, it is completely crippled. First, Darwin distorts the design process by falsely attributing to the environment the power to "select" traits. In fact, the ability to generate traits is a property of living things enabling them to diversify, multiply, and fill environments. Whether or not these traits fit an environment determines survival. Second, Darwin fails to explain how the ability to generate traits in living things—the real source of information for design—originated. This capacity is simply assimilated into "nature" through circular explanations.

A person looking for a natural cause of design is still left to rely on random mutations building enormous genetic information that "emerges" over time. Magic words and chance.

Yet, the Lord Jesus Christ still stands as the *best explanation* for the design that is built into living things. Just as the Bible says, "For the invisible things of him from the creation of the world are clearly seen, being understood by the things that are made" (Romans 1:20). ●

References
1. Mayr, E. 2001. *What Evolution Is.* New York: Basic Books 117.
2. Mayr, 118.
3. "Their DNA" would include variations of genes, recombination, mutations, lateral gene transfer, epigenetic factors, and other ways DNA diversity is increased.
4. "Beneficial variants" was a common description given by Darwin throughout his writings.
5. Waddington, C. 1960. Evolutionary Adaptations. In Yax, S., ed. *The Evolution of Life.* Chicago: University of Chicago Press, 385.
6. Mayr, 118.

Christians can be confident in claiming that the power of the Lord Jesus Christ is the best explanation for complex design found in nature, "for the invisible things of him from the creation of the world are clearly seen, being understood by the things that are made" (Romans 1:20). They also have an excellent scientific basis to know that creatures were made fully formed with innate abilities to diversify, multiply, fill, and fit their environments with great varieties of their kind.

The Evolutionist's Dilemma

Evolutionists must use words like "undirected" and "blind" to reinforce that natural selection, not God, creates nature's design. But an unavoidable side effect is that those same words hinder people from accepting evolution. They resist believing that any process that cannot "see" needs, is "blind" to natural forces, has "undirected" plans or goals, and relies heavily on chance, can create complex design.

This dilemma divides evolutionists. For

forceful retort to Senator Sam Brownback:

Brownback also presents the familiar creationist misrepresentation of evolution as a chance process, claiming that "man... is merely the chance product of random mutations." He doesn't seem to know that while mutations occur by chance, natural selection, which builds complex bodies by saving the most adaptive mutations, emphatically does not. Like all species, man is a product of both chance and lawfulness.[3]

Coyne's assertion sounds formidable

Natural Selection Is Not "Nature's Intelligence"

Evolutionists claim that creatures only appear to be designed since their existence is best explained by the interaction of genetic mutations and natural selection. Natural selection includes the capability for creatures to generate various heritable traits with varying degrees of impact on their survival. The key question to evolutionists is: What originally initiated this ability to generate traits? They claim natural selection produced it by working on nature's emergent properties (spontaneously created complexity).[1] This explanation is very weak—it is circular and invokes mystical environmental properties.

Evolutionists rely on ascribing an intention-to-act to the environment. They believe that for every trait in a creature, there is a corresponding environmental variable that caused it—such as polar bears' white fur and their arctic surroundings. The power behind variability is environmental, residing outside the creature.

This reveals why evolution advocates believe it is totally rational to explain that life's complexity results from the ever-upward pressure of natural selection's ability to see and save traits, though it, itself, is undirected and absolutely blind to any goal.

one faction, keeping naturalism pure from any hint of divine action is paramount. They do not flinch when asserting the almost exclusive role of blind chance. The other group's top goal is getting everybody to believe in evolution. They deftly downplay chance and push the concept that natural selection constructs methodically—in law-like fashion.[1] Human evolution is now touted as being "inevitable."[2] University of Chicago evolutionary biologist Jerry Coyne seems aware that people recoil from the suggestion that design results from chance. Note his

but is illegitimate. He attributes powers far beyond reality to environmental selection. He needs natural selection to behave lawfully, but it actually operates by chance, cannot see needs, and is too weak to halt the cumulative destructive effect of evolution's own fuel—mutations.

Environmental Processes Are Random

Unpredictable is the opposite of lawlike and is a far more accurate description of earth's environments. Any trait suitable, or advantageous, for one environment may be unsuitable the next year. This uncertainty is why Harvard's greatest evolutionist, Ernst Mayr, said, "In fact, nothing is predetermined. Furthermore, the objective of selection may change from one generation to the next, as environmental circumstances vary."[4]

Extinction is another phenomenon demonstrating how powers attributed to natural selection are fabricated. Evolution by natural selection means that groups of creatures change over time by a specific process that demands that gradual development and gradual extinction go hand in hand. Most extinction should result from the slow, steady, relative decrease in survival due to the inability to compete with offspring or rivals; but is this true?

Extinction is historically how species respond to unpredictable and drastic environmental changes—not to "bad" genes. No evidence shows that extinct classes of creatures were less fit to survive normal environmental hazards than kinds alive today. Substantial worldwide environmental fluctuations, well-documented geologically, are known to cause massive extinctions. These are augmented by intermediate environmental instabilities, like the Ice Age. Thus, extinction largely results from being in the wrong place at the wrong time. As Mayr said, "Chance may be particularly important in the haphazard survival during periods of mass extinction."[5]

Environmental changes and mutations are chance-driven occurrences that would not be expected to tend toward biological improvements. Prominent evolutionary paleontologist David Raup candidly observed of the fossil record: "It is not always clear, in fact it's rarely clear, that the descendants were actually better adapted than their predecessors. In other words, biological improvement is hard to find."[6] DNA studies reveal no consistent evolutionary trend toward increased genomic complexity.[7] Even plant offspring cloned from one parent and subject to the same starting soil conditions and environmental pressures have differing numbers of flowers and seeds.[8]

Other than wishful thinking, there has been no uncontested discovery of any creative, dynamic, emergent property or lawfulness imbued in environments. Environmental selection is not a non-random deterministic force; rather, a lot of chance events are observed. Nature tolerates many inferior horses without eliminating them; some seeds with superior genetics land on rocks while inferior ones land on good soil; environmental changes cause arbitrary extinctions; and accidents happen to even the best animals.

Environmental Processes Are Blind

Darwin idealized the all-seeing, god-like attribute associated with natural selection:

It may be said that natural selection is daily and hourly scrutinising, throughout the world, every variation, even the slightest; rejecting that which is bad, preserving and adding up all that is good; silently and insensibly working, whenever and wherever opportunity offers.[9]

This is not true. Environments do not "see" any individual gene. Even when environmental factors influence the genome, these interactions are managed by innate features in DNA. Natural selection cannot unequivocally identify which trait was the one "selected for" for an animal in any environment—but natural selection is purported to explain the origin of an animal's design by recounting the history of its traits. Thus,

Natural selection actually operates by chance, cannot see needs, and is too weak to halt the cumulative destructive effect of evolution's own fuel—mutations.

evolutionists increasingly claim that changes even down to the molecular level result from neutral evolution that proceeds untouched by natural selection.[10] Geneticists document that environments are powerless to eliminate most mutations. This buildup results in a total human genome degeneration of 1 to 2 percent per generation.[11]

Learning a Short Example

Is it reasonable to say that research has shown that, in the wild, natural selection of traits in any direction is so uncommon that it may not exist?

Yes. *The American Naturalist* published the largest analysis of the degree to which selection of changes of specific physical traits in an animal group affects their fitness—as measured by survival, mating success, and offspring. It tabulated 63 prior field studies covering 62 species and over 2,500 estimates of selection. Significance was obtained using statistical analysis and not opinions. The highest median correlation of trait selection to fitness was a low 16 percent. This means 84 percent

of changes were not explained by selection. Directional and stabilizing selection were no more likely to happen than non-directional and disruptive selection. In studies with species sample sizes greater than 1,000, the correlation of selection to survival was essentially negligible.[12]

Pulling It All Together

When constructing arguments for design, it is important to know why the only other explanation for intelligent design—natural selection—does not work. Research shows that environmental changes are just as random as mutations. But limits are necessary to the amount of luck allowed into science—otherwise, it degenerates into magic. Claims of unquantifiable emergent properties or lawfulness are equally mystical. Nevertheless, evolutionists claim reproductive abilities were not designed, but emerged by natural selection's powers to blindly see traits and lawfully save them with no final purpose to build complexity.

Christians must categorically push back the invalid claim that environments select organisms or even traits. This fallacy is essential to perpetuating evolutionary theory. No natural explanation exists for how creatures originally reproduced varieties of traits. It is not survival of the fittest, it is really survival of the "fitted." Creatures came designed with innate abilities to diversify, multiply, and fill environments. ●

References
1. For a thorough discussion, see Dennett, D. 1995. *Darwin's Dangerous Idea.* New York: Touchstone, 229-237.
2. Is Human Evolution Inevitable? Southern Methodist University press release, January 29, 2010, regarding lecture by Cambridge Professor Simon C. Morris titled "Darwin's Compass: Why the Evolution of Humans is Inevitable."
3. Coyne, J. 2007. Don't Know Much Biology. *Edge.* 212, June 6.
4. Mayr, E. Darwin's Influence on Modern Thought. *Scientific American.* July 2000, 81.
5. Mayr, E. 2001. *What Evolution Is.* New York: Basic Books, 281.
6. Raup, D. M. 1979. Conflicts Between Darwin and Paleontology. *Bulletin, Field Museum of Natural History.* 50 (1): 23.
7. Koonin, E. V. 2009. Darwinian evolution in the light of genomics. *Nucleic Acids Research.* 37 (4): 1011.
8. Millstein, R. L. Is the Evolutionary Process Deterministic or Indeterministic? An argument for Agnosticism. Presented at the Seventeenth Biennial Meeting of the Philosophy of Science Association, Vancouver, Canada, November 3, 2000.
9. Darwin, C. 1859. *On the origin of species by means of natural selection, or the preservation of favoured races in the struggle for life.* 1st edition, 1st issue. London: John Murray, 84.
10. Clements, A. et al. 2009. The reducible complexity of a mitochondrial molecular machine. *Proceedings of the National Academy of Sciences.* 106 (37): 15791.
11. Crow, J. F. 1997. The high spontaneous mutation rate: is it a health risk? *Proceedings of the National Academy of Sciences.* 94 (16): 8380.
12. Kingsolver, J. 2001. The Strength of Phenotypic Selection in Natural Populations. *The American Naturalist.* 157 (3): 245.

Suppose someone walks through their neighborhood and spies a new construction site for a custom-built home. Concrete has just been placed for the foundation. About how long ago did the project start?

Simply looking at how much work is in place would probably lead to a wrong answer. Actually, the project began—possibly years ago—within the mind of the designer. The designer's thoughts set the starting point, direction, and goal. His plan overrides everything. A radical new way to begin thinking about all constructed entities is that they mutually consist of items made out of matter, the *material* part, and their information for assembly, the *immaterial* part.

The new home's immaterial part consists of the designer's thoughts, concepts, ideas, and plans for achieving a specific goal.[1] What is amazing is that even though the designer's thoughts are not composed of space, time, or matter, they establish the initial context for which all additional information and all of the material parts will fit together and *make sense*.

For instance, this sentence first existed immaterially as a thought in a mind that sets the context for only adding letters as they fit to make a meaningful word. More words are added only as they fit the intent of this thought—which was to illustrate that discrete letters and words are meaningless unless organized in the context of a thought. The designer's ideas become the framework that is used in the material realm to direct all interactions of material things. Thus, ideas are incorporated into the home just as tangibly as lumber.

So, one of the earliest statements in a conversation about design in nature could be:

If I were to ask you to give me two pounds of your ideas, we know that cannot happen because even though your ideas are real things, they are also immaterial. Although thoughts are immaterial, they are crucial to any construction project since they set the starting point, direction, and goal. We need to find the best explanation for the immaterial information directing production of the diversity of life on earth.

Plans and Specifications Always Indicate Design

Man-made items are constructed following directions called plans and specifications. Specifications are a unique kind of writing designed to convey intent. They are written instructions that set advance constraints on precisely what, how, and when particular materials will be used. Plans show geometric details of where materials are placed (though there is overlap between the two). Together, they must be detailed and selective enough to accurately and unambiguously communicate intended fabrication information to obtain all the product's features.

Writing specifications and drawing plans can be difficult work. Designers are forced to initially build the project in their *minds*. They must visualize numerous details, and then clearly represent everything in that mental picture in words and drawings—a daunting task at any time, but especially for situations where no prototype even exists.

It is important to highlight two points about specifications. First, they are as close of a representation of the designer's thoughts as possible—but they are not the thoughts themselves. Thoughts exist independently of the paper or programs which convey them. Second, when plans or specifications exist for something, they are—without exception—a sign of conscious design. Why? They reveal an inten-

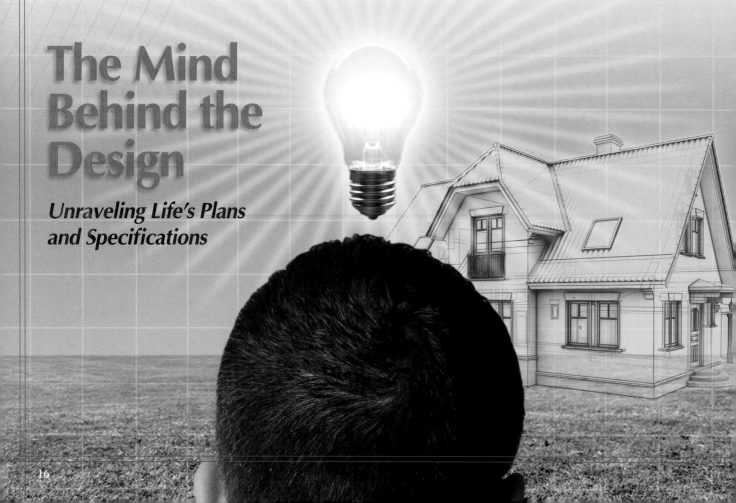

The Mind Behind the Design

Unraveling Life's Plans and Specifications

ional state that is characteristically restrictive. It selects in advance particular attributes for an intended purpose—which is the exact opposite of blind natural processes that yield random, ill-defined, piecemeal conglomerations of whatever is available.

So the secret to great architecture is not in the drawings, but in the mind of the architect. When evolutionary biologists determine the structure or sequence of DNA, they believe they uncover the secret of life.[2] Disregarding the fact that information is immaterial, they fixate on the material of DNA. But they are incorrect. Functioning just like specifications, DNA is manipulated by specialized proteins that enable it to transfer, transcribe, store, and recall information for building a living thing—but it is not the information. The real secret of life is the information.

Genetic Specifications Are Best Explained by Design

The evolutionist's explanation for the informational content in the first DNA (or RNA) relies initially on a random letter-by-letter increase. There are four letters in DNA or RNA language, and each one of the four letters has an equal chance of being the next letter in a genetic word. Building sequences of genetic words, which would constitute one gene, will ultimately be equivalent to writing a long paragraph in a book. Evolutionists insist that there was no plan to ensure the correct placement of any genetic letter or word, but that, over time, the first gene's informational content—the same as hundreds to thousands of meaningful words—would inevitably arise.

Creationists explain that genetic information originated in a thought that set the starting point, direction, and goal for a product. The thought was the scaffold upon which everything was built. It became the outline for the specific order found in genetic words—meaning that every letter and word is only valuable as it fits in the context of all of the other words, which themselves are constrained to satisfy the thought's purpose for the gene. Immaterial information and material DNA were created in creatures at the same time. Intelligent behavior is recognized by key features of a specification: (1) selecting (2) in

advance (3) exact attributes (4) for a purpose.

Learning a Short Example

It is possible that you may have a conversation with someone familiar with evolutionary beliefs. They may assert that the inability to identify the original source of biological information is just a gap in current scientific knowledge. Thus, it is arguing from ignorance to insist God fills the gap. Fortunately, some people who used this response have actually changed their minds following education as to why that thinking was more argumentative than analytical.

First, there is no ignorance. In universal human experience, when plans and specifications are encountered—meaning the causal record is known—they are always a product of intelligence. It is irrelevant that the operation of many processes is yet unknown. The source of information is not among them.

> In universal human experience, when plans and specifications are encountered—meaning the causal record is known—they are always a product of intelligence.

Second, all known natural processes oppose the notion that random genetic mutation and natural selection can generate information. Experiments show that randomly choosing letters one by one with no context to guide selection always generates *nonsense* regardless of how much time is utilized. (Be prepared for the evolutionist's comeback pushing the omnipotence of natural selection to set context and choose letters.[3]) So the very first specified genetic information capable of generating various physical traits cannot even get going.

Finally, when intelligent thought is placed head-to-head with random mutation/selection as a basis for information, intelligent thought has more scientific consistency to account for biological specification. Intelligent thought does not depend on mutation/selection being a poor explanation in order for it to be a better explanation.

Pulling It All Together

Many people will be amazed when they realize that their thoughts cannot be reduced to biology or even to atoms. After that fact captures attention, proceed by saying something like:

Since information is required for life but is immaterial, evolutionists have, thus far, failed to explain its origination strictly in terms of matter. They resist the fact that information always comes from a mind. Designers first build a project in their minds, then details go on paper. Specifications select exact features in advance of construction, reflecting intention and purpose—conclusive evidence of intelligent thought. Historically, every time people observe plans and specifications, their source is intelligence. So then, recognizing that the instructions to build a bird contain more information than the plans to build a jetliner, is it reasonable to believe that—only for the case of evolution—the laws of information are violated?

Let me suggest a better explanation that does not fight the facts. If you really want a refreshing way to contemplate graceful architecture, whether man-made or in nature, expand your appreciation to consider how much information was behind selecting and organizing those great building materials. Everything you see is actually fitted on a structure—a framework of unseen thoughts within a wonderful mind. Now, just conceive of the enormity of the mind that can visualize all at once all details for all life with all of their ecological interactions and write the specifications into a genetic alphabet consisting of only four letters. The Bible says that mind is the Lord Jesus Christ's and its infinite greatness is clearly seen by the things He has made (Romans 1:20). ●

References
1. Part of the thinking process, and a fundamental property of intelligent behavior, is creating ideas, intentions, forecasts, and goals. Yet, thus far, these things have not been shown to reduce down to the purely biological level since no coherent neural basis can account for them strictly within the interaction of action potentials between neurons. Some materialists question whether intentional states of the mind are even real. See Lycan, W. G. and G. Pappas. 1972. What is eliminative materialism? *Australasian Journal of Philosophy.* 50: 149-59; Rorty, R. 1970. In Defense of Eliminative Materialism. *Review of Metaphysics.* 24 (1): 112-121.
2. "We have discovered the secret of life." National Centre for Biotechnology Education. Posted on ncbe.reading.ac.uk, accessed March 31, 2010.
3. Guliuzza, R. 2010. Natural Selection Is Not "Nature's Design Process." *Acts & Facts.* 39 (4): 10-11; Guliuzza, R. 2010. Natural Selection Is Not "Nature's Intelligence." *Acts & Facts.* 39 (5): 10-11.

Discovering Life's Complex Patterns of Design

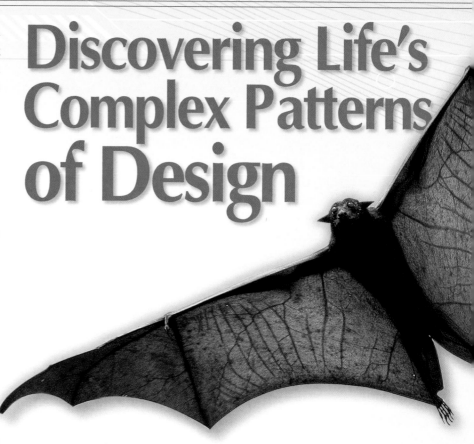

It is simple to learn a subtle method shared by evolutionists promoting evolution. Notice a common approach toward nature starting with Charles Darwin, who said in 1859:

I can see no very great difficulty...in believing that natural selection has converted the simple apparatus of an optic nerve merely coated with pigment and invested with transparent membrane, into an optical instrument.[1]

In May 2010, the current authority, Dr. Jerry Coyne, stated:

Bats evolved from small four-legged mammals, probably resembling shrews.... [S]election simply retooled the forelegs into wings, along with modifying the animal's weight, shape, musculature, nervous system and bones for flying (no feathers needed). One of the great joys of being a biologist is learning about the many species in nature whose evolution would appear, a priori, impossible.[2]

The approach they adopt is this: Attach the word "simple" to biological processes, anatomy, and, especially, presumed evolutionary changes. Why? Because simple changes made to simple creatures are more easily believed.

Via classrooms or television, the objective is to make all biological entities look very simple. So prompting someone to view the latest Discovery Channel episode about origins is a good way to start a conversation. Warn them that they will find the program drenched in words like "simple." To enhance careful listening, they should identify and tally the use of "simple words" or non-explanatory magic words—such as tissue "converted" into optical instruments or shrews being "retooled" into bats.

That bats are designed to fly is clearly seen, but seeing that is not the challenge. Evolutionists would have people replace their natural understanding that bats are very complicated—and thus, designed—with a belief that changing shrews to bats is simple, meaning bats only look designed, but really aren't.

To point people back to reality, creationists must learn to describe the organized features that are unique to complex things. Human study confirms that design is always the source of these features; furthermore, any part of any living creature reveals these features in abundance.

Recognizing Complex Patterns of Design

When someone watches a car engine run, they observe many *patterns of design*. Even though people can perceive a pattern, that does not mean they can readily transmit what they see through words. Help them make that mental connection by pointing out some basic patterns of design:

- Numerous interconnected parts
- Particular arrangement
- Proper alignment
- Moving parts
- Precise timing
- Exact dimensions and shape
- Tight fit
- Balance
- Definite sequence for correct assembly
- Synchronized coherent process

These patterns are found exclusively in human-designed items or living creatures—and none are simple. A useful way to express these patterns is to emphasize their operation. Thus, biologically complex entities demonstrate many intricately arranged elements (parts or multi-step processes) that are functionally interconnected to satisfy an intended purpose.

Identifying patterns indicating exact dimensions or precise timing is an *objective and verifiable* activity—plainly within scientific methodology. It is these elaborate relationships of parts in living systems that intrigue human researchers. In fact, a system can be identified as complex by the challenge it presents to an intelligent mind in deciphering the intricate interactions of its component parts.

A jumbled pile of car parts would not be considered complex, even though the odds of getting the parts in *that* particular arrangement may be low. When jumbling parts, some arrangement is a certainty. But in real life, complexity usually escalates rapidly with increasing numbers of distinct parts because, in order to work, a specific predetermined arrangement must be matched. It is the large number of specifically arranged parts that moves biological systems *mathematically* from the realm of simple to complex and greatly reduces—some mathematicians would say eliminates[3]—chance alone as an explanation.

Designers select words like "particular" or "exact" to restrict fabrication to specific traits. This type of information reflects *intent*—detected only in real design. Since intent *is* a hallmark of intelligence and *is not* a characteristic of natural environments, its presence allows a clear distinction for formulating questions, such as what best explains a bat's wings—are they a suitably specified feature intended for flight, or a purposeless retooling of forelegs into wings?

Environmental Processes Cannot Fashion Intricately Arranged Parts

The existence of complex biological features allows a test for their origins. This test only needs careful observation. However, it must be done right. Since the origination of how living things operate—especially their ability to generate diverse offspring—is the issue in dispute, ensure that it is not used as part of the explanation in any way. Stay alert to the evolutionist's habit of appealing to the living world's capabilities to explain its own origination. Thus, the cause of biological complexity for creationists is an intelligent mind, while for evolutionists it is chance coupled to environmental elements (sunlight, wind, rain, gravity, etc.).

The test is best utilized in conversation. Everyone should describe observations where environmental elements produce even two interconnected parts. Some chemical processes have a chance of going a few multiple steps. But, the discussion will make apparent the severe limitations of environmental elements—devoid of the living world's information.

Evolutionists correctly assert that natural processes alone can produce *ordered* arrangements. After molten aluminum cools, atoms naturally align into ordered lattices. But only after being worked into specifically shaped and precisely arranged parts can aluminum become a *complex* engine. While an ordered status has more structure than a chaotic one, it is far from the status of many intricately arranged parts. Thus, comparing order to biological complexity is irrelevant.

Many evolutionists claim the poor *quality* of living creatures proves they are not designed. But this is also beside the point.

Human-designed items range in quality from careless to extremely fine. Words describing quality, such as "seamless," "blemish free," or "durable," are qualifiers that add weight to correctly perceiving patterns of design—but so do words like "crude" or "sloppy." Quality in itself is not the sign of intellectual activity. Several points flow from this fact: 1) Genuine design does not demand anything be of the best quality; 2) in their prime, living things normally do exhibit breathtaking fit and finish; and 3) environmental elements alone do not achieve even shoddy design—since they cannot produce *any* design.

Learning a Short Example

A March 2010 episode of the popular series *Life* on the Discovery Channel was about mammals. On the origin of bats, it stated, "Up close it's easy to see that this is a mammal. Bats evolved about 50 million years ago, probably from a small squirrel-like mammal that had learned to glide through the air. From there it was only a hop, skip, and a jump to true flight."[4] Is this, or Dr. Coyne's account of how "selection simply retooled" a shrew, what someone should actually believe about bats?

> The large number of specifically arranged parts moves biological systems *mathematically* from the realm of simple to complex and greatly reduces—some mathematicians would say eliminates—chance alone as an explanation.

Helping someone recognize obvious patterns of design—in just the bat's wing—may provide a more realistic explanation. Bat wings integrate unique properties in regard to composition, shape, and movement. In flight, tremendously elastic wing skin is cyclically folded close to the body, then rapidly extended in precisely coordinated motions. Extremely synchronized rapid twitch muscles deftly modulate bone interactions at dozens of joints, allowing subtle alterations of wing shape. Thus, at slow speeds, bats generate more lift and greater maneuverability than many birds. Even evolutionary descriptions of the supposedly earliest bat fossils, *Onychonycteris finneyi* or *Icaronycteris*, are like living

bats in every aspect—though a few features were scraped together that they envision to be "primitive."[5]

Pulling It All Together

Helping someone discover patterns of design can be exciting. A brief description could be:

When I drive my car, I observe many organized features that are patterns consistent with design. There are interdependent parts and lots of moving parts, arranged in a particular order, with very precise shape, alignment, and timing. A single human cell has the same precise fit and timing, but also finely-tuned feedback loops for self regulation, a materials packaging and delivery system, a microscopic railway system, hundreds of communication pathways, and information stored, retrieved, and translated as a functioning language. Features like these are only found in human-designed items and living things. No known environmental elements *alone* can produce such interconnected parts.

I recently saw a program where the origination of these things all the way up to flight abilities of bats was portrayed as very simple. If you start looking for the word "simple" in evolution-based education, you may be shocked at how often it is used. Simple changes made to simple creatures are more easily believed, but in real life biologically complex entities have many intricately arranged parts that are functionally interconnected to satisfy an intended purpose. The best explanation for this still remains the infinite power of the Lord Jesus Christ, who packed all of this complexity into creatures whose workmanship stands unequaled. ◉

References
1. Darwin, C. 1859. *On the origin of species.* London: John Murray, 218
2. Coyne, J. The Improbability Pump. *The Nation*, May 10, 2010.
3. The Wistar Institute Symposium at Philadelphia, PA, in April 1966 was the first forum in which mathematicians exchanged findings challenging Darwinian theory. See Schützenberger, M. 1967. Algorithms and the neo-darwinian theory of evolution. *Mathematical Challenge to the Neodarwinian Theory of Evolution.* Monograph No. 5 Wistar Institute Press, 73-80. See also Hoyle, F. 1984. *The Intelligent Universe.* New York: Holt, Rinehart and Winston, 17.
4. *Life: Mammals.* First aired on Discovery Channel on March 28, 2010.
5. Simmons, N. et al. 2008. Primitive Early Eocene bat from Wyoming and the evolution of flight and echolocation. *Nature.* 451 (7180): 818-821.

Life's Indispensable Microscopic Machines

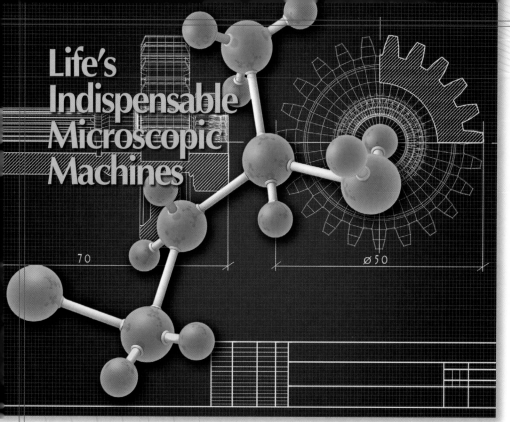

70   Ø50

ies, motors, brakes, shafts, rods, hooks, bearings, bushings, springs, end caps, valves, seals, plugs, rivets, spot-welded joints, mounts, and braces. These are fitted together by other molecules that act like templates, work benches, clamps, and vises. Yet other molecules take the final products where they are trimmed, folded, and set to be activated. Another molecular work station will package, label, and transport products to their correct destinations. After the machine's useful life is ended, another apparatus will engulf it, break it down, and send the components back for recycling.

Molecular Machines Are Best Explained by Design

The microscopic size of these machines is vital to systematically fine-tune dozens of molecular properties. For example, many molecular motors must work cooperatively to transform molecular movements to visually detectable levels. All of these features are detailed in advance and the information is stored in the DNA's plans and specifications.

In a typical kitchen, there are food processors, blenders, and mixers. In some ways they *look* similar, but their capabilities actually have little overlap. Each machine has a *primary* function which it performs well based on the speed and manner in which its parts interact. These parts fit tightly together, which means that though a few blender and mixer parts have exactly the same function, one cannot just swap them. In similar manner, the parts of molecular machines are meticulously fitted together for their primary purpose. Many function in totally unique roles that are critical for life. And some cannot lose a single part or exchange parts with other machines without that machine—and the entire organism—breaking down.

In most people's minds, the words "machine" and "designed" belong together, so just knowing that complex cellular machines exist is sufficient evidence to make that connection. But others are stuck in evolutionary explanations for the origination of molecular machines. It would be beneficial to know why this thinking is

H umans love machines. Everyone likes how they save time and make jobs easier. If a new machine is invented that helps detect specific diseases and aids in early diagnosis, it is big news.

People also enjoyed watching machines operate before their many moving parts were covered up for safety reasons. Now, TV programs that slice machines apart so people can look inside are popular. So it is likely that someone would listen intently if a Christian were to describe some real microscopic machines right inside *their own bodies* working to keep them alive.

Be assured that helping anybody learn of these intricate, minute machines will be a powerful testimony of the Lord Jesus' "invisible" qualities, like His endless power and intellect, that are clearly seen by the things He has made (Romans 1:20.)

Cellular Life Operates with Machines

Begin by showing that cellular machines, like man-made machines, consist of numerous interconnected moving parts that function together for an intended purpose—but are far superior. Functioning in repetitive mechanical cycles, cellular machines have chemical mol-

ecule "parts" that usually switch between two different—but still very precise—shapes in a strictly controlled manner. Like any motor, they convert fuel into kinetic energy to *make things move* in specific directions. A few examples are:

- DNA maintenance robots that proofread information, unwind the double helix, cut out defects, splice in corrections, and rewind the strands
- Intracellular elevators
- Mobile brace-builders that construct distinct internal tubular supports
- Spinning generators that move molecules from low to high energy states
- Ratchet devices that convert random molecular forces to linear motion
- Motors that whirl hair-like structures like an outboard motor
- A microscopic railroad with engines and tracks

Finally, describe *how* the machines are made to reinforce awareness of the total design process. Ask your acquaintance to visualize an assembly plant that is so advanced and so small that dozens could fit on the head of a pin. The energy to run both the assembly plants and machines is finely tunable and supplied by sunlight, molecular motions, heat, electricity, or chemical conversions.

Machine parts themselves are complex molecules corresponding to switches, batter-

better at rationalizing than explaining.

Evolutionists Submit Implausible Explanations

When looking at the evolutionist's best scientific journals for explanations specifically on the origins of molecular machines, stay alert for extraordinary extrapolations.[1] For instance, if a window fan is the machine under investigation in one of these papers, be prepared to look for this predictable pattern:

Finding: Researchers discover that fans have electric motors that spin blades to move air.

Conclusion: Air conditioners are simple derivations of fans because they also have electric motors that spin blades—notwithstanding an air conditioner's unique motor, blades, compressor, condenser, evaporator, and thermostat.

The exaggeration is assured. Why? Since researchers *find* only one fully functioning machine or another, evolutionary *conclusions* of how, in the remote past, parts from one molecular machine morphed into another will always be conjectures inferred greatly beyond what the findings support.

These papers survive peer review still containing extraordinary extrapolations that sidestep real explanations for the arrival of fundamentally distinct parts, instead depicting molecular parts as (somehow) having been stripped from primary functions elsewhere in the cell and spontaneously re-assembled into new machines. Critics point out that those great gaps of information make the evolutionary path unbelievable. Note how these weaknesses are merely dismissed when a top evolutionary authority like Dr. Jerry Coyne says, "It is not valid, however, to assume that, because one man cannot imagine such pathways, they could not have existed."[2] Be content in recognizing that those types of responses cannot be satisfied with scientific answers.

Lacking experimental evidence supporting their explanations about molecular machines, evolutionists have turned to a firm belief that if it can be imagined, it could happen. In conversation, highlight this disconnect. Point out that, given the extreme precision of these machines, evolutionary accounts

must repeatedly use three words not normally associated with precision: "recruited,"[3] "cobbled,"[4] and "tinkered."[5]

Thus, evolutionists believe in a simplistic scenario where "the necessary pieces for one particular cellular machine...were lying around long ago. It was simply a matter of time before they came together into a more complex entity,"[6] upon which natural selection tinkered away at cobbling together borrowed parts for millions of years. Aside from the magical whimsy, this explanation is like saying cars originated when an engine was coupled to a transmission, which was mounted to a chassis, and so forth. Leaving another major unanswered question—where did the engine, transmission, and chassis come from?

Learning a Short Example

Do evolutionists really recognize the intricacies of molecular machines yet attribute their origins to ill-defined forces? Princeton University researchers recently described a

> Cellular machines, like man-made machines, consist of numerous interconnected moving parts that function together for an intended purpose—but are far superior.

theory to explain how some cellular machines enable organisms to rapidly adapt to environmental stresses. The report detailed elaborate principles guiding cooperation between machines that was "analogous to a car's cruise control or a home's thermostat."

[Lead study author Raj] Chakrabarti said, "Control theory offers a direct explanation for an otherwise perplexing observation and indicates that evolution is operating according to principles that every engineer knows." The scientists do not know how the cellular machinery guiding this process may have originated, but they emphatically said it does not buttress the case for intelligent design, a controversial notion that posits the existence of a creator responsible for complexity in nature.[7]

An alternative explanation exists that

actually fits with observed origins of every other machine. The information for the parts and construction of "cruise control"-style molecular machines was the result of real design with the intent of enabling organisms to diversify, multiply, and fill new environments.

Pulling It All Together

The best way to appreciate machines is to watch them. Unfortunately, pictures of molecular machines are rare and drawings most likely will not be available during spontaneous conversations. But using words to build mental pictures of these incredible miniature machines can be effective. Human minds powerfully connect machines to design. People know that while some animals may use tools, only humans build machines.

For that reason, a conversation could be very engaging since it may be the first disclosure to most people of the existence of these machines. Why? Because in evolution-based education, not all scientific findings are equally welcome and, thus, are subject to being selectively promoted. The above frenzied foot-stomping denial of the research's obvious implication shows that getting people to believe in evolution is a higher priority than learning.

Revealing this convoluted thinking that *does* attribute precise microscopic machines to blind tinkering—but *not* to design—will let it be seen for what it is. So, go ahead and tell someone about these life-sustaining little machines. They may build the bridge for someone to find eternal life in their life-giving Creator. ◉

References
1. See Clements, A. et al. 2009. The reducible complexity of a mitochondrial molecular machine. *Proceedings of the National Academy of Sciences*. 106 (37): 15791-15795.
2. Coyne, J. A. 1996. God in the details. *Nature*. 383 (6597): 227-8.
3. McLennan, D. 2008. The Concept of Co-option: Why Evolution Often Looks Miraculous. *Evolution: Education and Outreach*. 1 (3): 247-258.
4. Hersh, B. and S. B. Carroll. 2005. Direct regulation of *knot* gene expression by Ultrabithorax and the evolution of cis-regulatory elements in *Drosophila*. *Development*. 132: 1567-1577.
5. Clements, 15793. Also Jacob, F. 1977. Evolution and tinkering. *Science*. 196 (4295): 1161-1166.
6. Report on Clements' *PNAS* article (reference 1). Keim, B. More 'Evidence' of Intelligent Design Shot Down by Science. *Wired Science*. Posted on wired.com August 27, 2009, accessed June 5, 2010.
7. MacPherson, K. Evolution's new wrinkle: Proteins with 'cruise control' provide new perspective. Princeton University news release, November 10, 2008, reporting on research published in Chakrabarti, R. et al. 2008. Mutagenic Evidence for the Optimal Control of Evolutionary Dynamics. *Physical Review Letters*. 100: 258103.

All-or-Nothing Unity

Which came first, the chicken or the egg? A fresh usage of this familiar question can quickly illustrate unseen strengths to the design argument. At first, the issue seems to be one of timing. That problem is real, but so is the need for the *parts* for the chicken or egg, the *information*, and *conditions* of these to be:

1) available,
2) localized,
3) capable of functioning together,
4) for a purpose, and, of course,
5) at the right time.

It doesn't matter whether the goal is the chicken or the egg; the absence of the information, conditions, or any vital part is a definite show-stopper. The chicken/egg scenario—symbolic of any reproducing organism—is really about the absolute unity of certain vital parts to vital functions.

In regard to function, designers need to know if all, some, or none of it is maintained without the full set of parts. They know that some aspects of their project can be built by increments, but at certain phases *all* of those parts must be collected together and built together or *none* of that specific function can be obtained. In the living world, these are called "vital" parts.

The fact that *all-or-nothing* unity exists cannot be ignored—especially when the known source is always real design. So, when all-or-nothing unity is found in the living world, the reasonable conclusion is that it is evidence of a real Designer's work.

Explaining the Vital Unity of Parts and Function

It is not difficult to present the case for all-or-nothing unity. A powerful, yet easily understood, statement is this: In organisms, some parts are so important to the function of life that if they are missing, life stops. Excellent examples are found for certain molecules, organs, and systems, but the explanation of these can get complicated. So the difficulty is deciding on a great example.

Thinking biblically, it is notable that Genesis' account of the first and foremost unified biologically vital system, reproduction, is absolutely contrary to classic evolutionary origins of this core process. It cannot be overstated that for evolution to proceed, it is not enough just to attain some physiological function—what is needed is *reproductive* life. Fortunately, when engaging in conversation, reproduction is a science topic where almost everyone has some knowledge.

Using reproduction as the example of all-or-nothing unity in a conversation is powerful. For the first time, most listeners will hear something that totally defies evolutionary dogma. They will be astounded to learn that the minimum number of parts necessary for an organism to reproduce is—*the organism itself.* The whole organism is vital. This is scientific fact. It doesn't mean that every part is vital, but it does mean that only the organismal unit encompasses all of the critical *parts, information,* and *conditions* necessary to reproduce itself according to the constraints of its life cycle.

There is no scientific evidence showing some organisms as "primitive" and some as "advanced." Life forms are just *different,* with most being extraordinarily complex. So, in order for the single-cell bacteria, believed by evolutionists to be thoroughly primitive, to reproduce by fission, budding, or fragmentation—the bacteria itself is needed. Yet, in order to produce a human baby, a man and a woman, and all of their vital interdependent parts, are the essentials—science has shown that it cannot be broken down to any smaller level.

Another advantage of using reproduction as an example of all-or-nothing unity is that it underscores the impotence of an iterative evolutionary process—dependent on procreative processes—to explain the origin of reproduction. How do organisms "arise" by increments until they can reproduce?

This fact is so indicting that evolutionists will push back with all kinds of arguments, but they will all cheat in their explanations. Every example given will always start and end by using some vital things from the organism itself, to be looking for this. For example, yes, there is in-vitro fertilization, but that starts with donor egg and sperm and the embryo is returned to the normal realm of development.

Evolutionists Publish Insufficient Explanations

When in conversation, be assured that evolutionists will fail to explain the *origins* of biological information and reproduction. Point out how they simply skip explaining a main biological feature by always starting with reproducing entities.

The literature has avoided detailed explanations of all-or-nothing unity for the vital parts of reproduction. For instance, most people could do a search for the evolutionary origins of mammal reproduction. They will uncover claims that it began as a simple alteration from an egg-laying reptilian system. But details of how the changes could happen are missing. And what about the origin of a mammal's life-sustaining milk ducts? The literature states that these slowly arose from "modified sweat glands"—without a second thought of an offspring's nutritional needs pending modification.

The best evolution-based journals have published replies to all-or-nothing unity for other parts of organisms.[1] However, these articles have *all* claimed that the solution to all-or-nothing unity lies in researchers imagining where similar—not always identical—parts could be borrowed ("co-opted," "pre-adapted," or "recruited") from existing objects. Even if borrowed parts could work, which is doubtful, only condition one, availability, is satisfied. The necessary information and other four conditions are not even addressed. Thus, by taking an *indirect* path to all-or-nothing unity, these responses not only fail to engage the true issue, but also demonstrate how imagination cannot substitute for testable findings.

Learning a Short Example

If the iterative evolutionary mechanism is crushed by the ultimate circular dilemma—it takes an organism to produce an organism—and only God can break the circle, then why did headlines recently declare, "Scientists create a living organism"? Can it really be that complex if "scientists have turned inanimate chemicals into a living organism that raises profound questions about the essence of life"?[2] Actually, the complexity is staggering.

After 15 years and $40 million invested, results of the ongoing project—published with abundant hyperbole in *Science*[3]—simply confirmed that the minimum number of vital parts to make a bacterium is a bacterium. As it relates to life, these researchers copied DNA code of one species, added four segments of human-derived code, inserted this genome into a DNA-emptied nucleus of a similar bacterium, and, voila, it reproduced. They "created" neither the information nor vital conditions, but were obliged to utilize an existing cell and plagiarized genetic code.[4]

> The fact that *all-or-nothing* unity exists cannot be ignored—especially when the known source is always real design.

The Bible has a far more scientifically accurate explanation for the origin of reproduction. In Genesis 1:11, the first biological entities are those "whose seed is in itself." Not only is the origin of all-or-nothing unity answered, but the Hebrew meaning of "seed" correctly presents reproduction as a unified whole. This one word summarizes the act of sowing, that which is sown, and the product of sowing, which contains yet more indispensable seed. The necessary conditions, parts, and information converge—an event distinctive of real design, not random forces of nature—enabling organisms to diversify, multiply, and fill new environments.

Pulling It All Together

Darwin knew the exceeding improbability of unintelligent natural forces alone building life's complexity. His theory attempts to beat the odds one tiny bit at a time, and hence is limited by:

- Life *being* "evolvable," meaning organisms can reproduce and offspring have diverse traits.
- The environment's ability to see, select, and save organisms' favorable traits.
- Environmental powers acting on traits to incrementally increase complexity over many generations, thus making organisms only *look* like they were designed.

Use all-or-nothing unity, particularly in reproduction, to confront evolution's attempt to chip away at prohibitive improbability and explain biological design.

- Reproduction is one of many processes revealing that *all* necessary conditions, parts, and information must come together *or nothing* of the function is achieved—a distinctive of real design.
- Scenarios depicting organisms arising incrementally are implausible since the minimum number of parts necessary for an organism to reproduce is the *organism itself*.
- Evolutionary explanations cheat. Reproductive origins are not explained, they start with replicating life.
- Natural selection, Darwin's substitute god, has no ability to see, select, act on, favor, or operate as an agent of change.

Why should anyone believe that the living world only looks like it is designed, but really isn't? In fact, the design in the living world is such that it *resists* being explained by natural causes. All scientific evidence shows that creatures come programmed with innate abilities to reproduce after their kind, but not with strictly identical offspring, in order to diversify, multiply, and fill new environments. The Bible clearly says not only that the Lord Jesus Christ designed life, but also reveals how He did it: the chicken was created "whose seed [egg or sperm] was in itself"—all at one time. ●

References
1. See Clements, A. et al. 2009. The reducible complexity of a mitochondrial molecular machine. *Proceedings of the National Academy of Sciences.* 106 (37): 15791-15795.
2. Cookson, C. Scientists create a living organism. *Financial Times.* Posted on ft.com May 20, 2010, accessed July 12, 2010.
3. Gibson, D. G. et al. 2010. Creation of a Bacterial Cell Controlled by a Chemically Synthesized Genome. *Science.* 329 (5987): 52-56.
4. See Thomas, B. Have Scientists Created a Synthetic Cell? *ICR News.* Posted on icr.org May 27, 2010, accessed June 28, 2010.

"I'm related to George Washington," an acquaintance announced after searching his genealogical record. He also believes he is closely related to chimpanzees. Though he doesn't really look like either, all three do share a lot of similar features.

So, are similar looks or features enough to establish whether these three are related closely, remotely, or not at all in regard to their ancestry? No. Similar looks and features can be very deceiving. A true relationship is actually a *fact-based* connection. A line of connected birth certificates is factual evidence that can be verified. Just comparing similar features—or even DNA—to determine related ancestry is always an *inference* with a probability of being right ranging from high to zero.

If all organisms had completely different features, there might not be any discussion of them being related by common descent. However, evolutionists have effectively sold the idea that when people see similarities, they actually "see" remnants of common ancestry. Seeing something carries emotional links. So persuading an evolutionist, who feels deep down inside that all life is somehow connected, to replace his inference-based account of similarities with a design-based explanation is challenging.

The good news is the Bible's assurance that the Lord's designs in nature are "clearly seen" (Romans 1:20), which means that His creative witness has real power to cause blinded minds (2 Corinthians 4:4) to see truth.

Homology: Another Circular Evolutionary Concept

Related—a word that could mean sharing common attributes or common ancestry.

Cataloging common attributes is generally objective scientific inquiry, but explaining their origin through common ancestry is subjective. Before Darwin, the common attributes shared by different types of, say, fish or birds were useful for classifying the living things of nature. But they were only that—common attributes.

When discussing the similar features of organisms with friends, it is important to first point out that all that can be definitively claimed about them scientifically is that they are

Similar Features Show Design, Not Universal Common Descent

similar—which may or may not be relevant. Be prepared to avoid getting sidetracked and stay on topic. The issues are explaining where structures originally come from, and whether there is a scientifically plausible mechanism that can change one kind of creature into a fundamentally different kind of creature.

Next, point out that for Darwin and his followers, it is only *self evidence* that similar features are explained by common descent. For them, this is an axiom—an obvious truth—not needing outside experimental validation.

In 1859, Darwin's explanation was more like dogma: "The similar framework of bones in the hand of a man, wing of a bat, fin of the porpoise, and leg of the horse…and innumerable other such facts, at once *explain themselves* on the theory of descent with slow and slight successive modification."[1] In even today's best scientific journals, the treatment is unchanged. Thus, common ancestry is the *explanation* for common attributes and common attributes are the *evidence* of common ancestry.

Just like "natural selection" and "survival of the fittest," common ancestry is the self-apparent explanation for common features only because the thinking is circular. Circular arguments are naturally self-certifying. In this case, circularity has even advanced to the point of definition. "Although ancestry was at first viewed only as an explanation for homology [similar features], it soon was incorporated into the definition."[2]

Similar Features Mean Common Ancestry… Except When They Don't

"Inconsistent" is the best word to stress in conversations to describe how evolutionists compare similar features among organisms. This is because similar features are just that—similar—and the myriad of combinations that organisms possess does not necessarily fit branching evolutionary trees. If evolutionists believe a similar feature is from a common ancestor, it is due to "divergent evolution." And if organisms share a similar feature *not* due to common ancestry, it is conveniently called "convergent evolution."

Scientific-sounding lingo is substituted for data to explain why organisms with essentially no common ancestry have extraordinarily similar features, like the camera-like eye shared by squids and humans. At the same time, other facts are selectively deemphasized about organisms that are presumed to be very closely related and yet do not share some surprisingly important features, such as humans having a muscle that moves the thumb's tip that chimpanzees don't have.

The main point is that explanations for the presence or absence of similar features are totally arbitrary. For example, evolutionists assert that whales' distinctive body shape evolved from a lineage of land mammals that slowly readapted to aquatic life. Consider how the leading journal *Science* elected to pick-and-choose between conflicting features, either molecular or shapes of parts (called "morphology"), to support this theory:

> Despite this evidence that cetaceans [whales] evolved from artiodactyls [even-toed mammals like deer, sheep, and pigs], substantial discrepancies remain. If cetaceans belong to artiodactyls, then similarities in the cranial and dental morphologies of mesonychians [extinct carnivorous mammals] and cetaceans must be a result of convergent evolution or must have been lost in artiodactyls. Furthermore, molecular data favor a sister-group relationship between whales and hippopotami. This conflicts with the conventional view based on morphology that hippopotami are closer to other artiodactyls than they are to whales.[3]

If features do not conform to preconceived thinking, that is because they could represent "divergence," "convergence," "character reversals," "vestiges," "rudiments," "independent losses," "one-time gains," "parallel derivatives," or any of the jargon tagged to subjective evolutionary explanations. Comparing fossils based on similar features suffers from the same trap of circular reasoning, and gene sequence comparisons suffer from the same prejudices, inconsistencies, and excuses. In fact, comparing different sequences from the *same* organism can lead to very different presumed evolutionary relationships. These facts provide a conversational opportunity to highlight the plastic-like attribute of evolutionary theory to absorb all observations—even ones that are totally contradictory.

Learning a Short Example

Do evolutionists really approach similar features inconsistently? Consider a report on genetic research for the trait of echolocation:

> The discovery represents an unprecedented example of adaptive sequence convergence between two highly divergent groups....[Study author Stephen Rossiter stated] "it is generally assumed that most of these so-called convergent traits have arisen by different genes or different mutations. Our study shows that a complex trait—echolocation—has in fact evolved by identical genetic changes in bats and dolphins."... [I]f you draw a phylogenetic [relationship] tree...based on similarities in the prestin [a hearing gene] sequence alone, the echolocating bats and whales come out together rather than with their rightful evolutionary cousins....[Rossiter added], "We were surprised by...the sheer number of convergent changes in the coding DNA."[4]

> { Just like "natural selection" and "survival of the fittest," common ancestry is the self-apparent explanation for common features only because the thinking is circular. }

So, based on conflicting similarities in shapes of body parts, fossils, or genes, are deer, sheep, pigs, extinct wolf-like animals, hippopotami, or bats the bona fide "rightful evolutionary cousins" of whales? Also note how the gene sequence similarities—which have nothing to do with common ancestry—are utterly dismissed as a simple convergence of fortuitous mutations.

Pulling It All Together

Armed with facts, believers can provide open-minded listeners with information regarding similar features that they will never get from evolution-based textbooks, teachers, or television. A brief conversation may go something like this:

Granted, humans do look more like chimpanzees than horses. That is why evolutionists regularly claim that we are cousins.

Similar features are probably the best evidence for evolution, but they really turn out to be a big problem. First, only focusing on similar features sidetracks discussion from the main issue evolutionists have failed to explain, which is where the complex information and molecular construction machinery to make any feature on any creature originated. Simply claiming that they got it from their "older relative" begs the question and is not an explanation. This leads to the next problem.

Evolutionists assert the self-evidence that similar features show relationships. By assuming the truth of a claim that they should be proving, evolutionists end up in this inescapable tangle of circular thinking: Similar features are derived from common ancestry and the best evidence for common ancestry is similar features. Darwin disregarded the circularity of his argument, just as his followers do today.

Even more revealing is that evolutionists never tell us that there really are not tidy, logical threads of traits from a common ancestor down all the paths to different types of creatures—forcing them to pick and choose which traits to showcase or to make excuses. In truth, creatures share some traits with other creatures—"related" or not. Comparing organisms' traits actually shows patchwork similarity. That is why humans have some traits that are similar to chimpanzees, but other traits just as—or more—similar to orangutans, gibbons, guinea pigs, other animals, and even plants.

Given the failure of evolution to prove you are related to chimpanzees, shouldn't you consider starting a worthwhile relationship with your Creator, the Lord Jesus Christ? For those related to Him by faith, He prayed, "Father, I will that they also, whom thou hast given me, be with me where I am; that they may behold my glory" (John 17:24). ●

References
1. Darwin, C. 1872. *The Origin of Species By Means of Natural Selection*, 6th ed. London: John Murray, 420, emphasis added.
2. Donoghue, M. 1992. Homology. In *Keywords in Evolutionary Biology*. Keller, E. F. and E. A. Lloyd, eds. Cambridge, MA: Harvard University Press, 171.
3. Rose, K. D. 2001. Evolution: The Ancestry of Whales. *Science*. 293 (5538): 2216-2217.
4. In Bats and Whales, Convergence in Echolocation Ability Runs Deep. *ScienceDaily*. Posted on sciencedaily.com, accessed August 10, 2010. A report on research published in *Current Biology*.

Similar Features Demonstrate Common Design

There are two equally valid explanations for why some things share similar features. They may be part of a group, like motorcycles, "related" by commonly designed attributes. Or, like brothers, they may be related by common ancestry. After setting this premise, you can ask someone, "Do you know that evolutionists refuse to even look at evidence for common design, regardless of its scientific merits, because (as an eminent Harvard evolutionist asserted) they 'cannot let a divine foot in the door'?"[1]

Some people will be surprised by the deliberate unscientific practices of evolutionists—which opens the door to the next question: "Have you ever heard why similar features are better explained by common design than common ancestry?"

Recognizing "Purpose" Opens Minds

The answer may liberate their minds to see more clearly what actually happens in nature. "Purpose" is the key word to expose how evolutionary philosophy first constrains, then distorts normal thinking. Evolutionists are adamant that the purpose of, say, a bat's wings *cannot* be known. Be assured that they do see—actually quite clearly, according to Romans 1:20—the purpose of things in nature. But admitting purpose would imply intent, whose source has only been observed from intelligence. Thus, a tenet of atheistic evolutionary faith—rather than scientific evidence—forces evolutionists to willfully suppress the normal conclusions about purpose.

For evolutionists, bats just happen to have structures that just happen to "function" for flight—thinking that lacks coherence in any other realm. So it is now understandable why, for even extensive phenomena, the confined evolutionist's mind can entertain only one explanation and then shuts down. As evolutionary authority Stephen Gould pronounced, "Why should a rat run, a bat fly, a porpoise swim, and I type this essay with structures built of the same bones unless we all inherited them from a common ancestor?"[2]

Gould may refuse to recognize purpose, but most people will not. Help them to consider a vital, overarching purpose the Lord gave to all creatures—declared after *both* creation and the Flood (Genesis 1:22, 28; 8:17; 9:1, 7)—which was to *fill the earth*. So Gould's question has at least another explanation. It is not the bones, per se, but the distinctive shapes, control, and arrangements of the appendages—united with all of their other internal variability—that enable them to occupy environments.

A person must be willing to embrace three *radical departures* from evolutionary thinking.

- Stop looking to the extrinsic environment coupled to natural selection to explain the origin and primary source of adaptive capability, and start looking to the *built in* diversifying reproductive power of organisms. Environments do not select organisms for habitation. Rather, organisms occupy environments when *they* generate traits that fit.
- Drop the evolutionarily-tainted belief that answers to what causes adaptive change can be reduced to one or several components (e.g., DNA) of organisms—a fallacy basic to assertions of bit-by-bit origins from individual parts—and begin treating the *entire organism* as the minimum component necessary to reproduce, adapt, and fill environments.
- Embrace the *search for purpose* as a guide for biological research to encourage the broadest array of questions and testing of all possible explanations.

Changed thinking allows people to see nature as it really operates. One benefit is the liberty to treat Gould's question fairly and consider all possible explanations.

A Better Explanation for Similar Features

It is better to approach design based on the biblical biological facts presented in Genesis 1:11-30—that the reproductive and adaptive capacity or "seed" of an organism *was always programmed* "in itself" to reproduce "after its kind" so that the organism could be "fruitful [divide/branch into diverse progeny] and multiply" to deliberately pioneer or "fill" environments of "the earth." This whole-organism based approach is far more scientifically accurate.

Any explanation must explain these observations: diversity within, and similar features between, kinds of organisms; and stasis, meaning a fossil and its living counterpart show remarkably little change.[3] Biological life is *fundamentally discontinuous*, meaning organisms fit *only one* phylum, class, and order. Common descent explanations generally clash with these observations.

However, the premise that structures in many life forms are manufactured for similar purposes but applied in different environments is very plausible. Electric motors powering a toy train or subway operate by the same principles and may have similar parts made from the same materials. But it is the *specification that regulates manufacturing* of unique shapes and arrangements that allows them to fit specific applications.

So, knowing that organisms, per their kind, must generate traits to thrive on the same planet but occupy diverse niches, several biological predictions would be:

1. Similar features could be based on similar design to fulfill similar purposes.
2. Body forms are tied directly to embryonic development.
3. Developmental pathways, therefore, would have some similarities.
4. Some major similarity in genes for regulating development and proteins would be found in many organisms.
5. Extreme multi-step specified regulation over thousands of details is of utmost importance to produce unique organisms that yet may have similar overall plans.
6. Thus, multiple layers of hierarchical information and machinery exist.
7. For any kind of organism, internal abilities to reproduce diverse offspring will not be explained in the cellular machinery, nor solely in genetics, nor fully encompassed in information of developmental paths, but found as a unit that cannot be reduced lower than the organism itself.

This is what is found. Organisms are programmed to adapt to fill environmental niches. Genetics and developmental pathways help control embryonic development of similarity in form from flies to dinosaurs. But flies are flies because of uniquely specified developmental controls. This information is previously encoded in the entire organism—not just the genes—to control embryonic develop-

ment. Reproduction transmits the entire system to the next generation.

Learning a Short Example

Prediction five is important and illustrates how to treat similar genetic sequences. Complex regulatory networks control cells during embryologic development and thereafter. Networks are intracellular logic paths. Say an organism needs a protein coded by a gene. Management of genes may be controlled by other DNA called a "promoter." Control of the promoter is achieved by other products (either DNA or proteins) called "regulators" that can activate *or* suppress promoters. Often, multiple regulators control promoters, and they may control each other via internal logic strategies like "AND gates" or "OR gates," which may

. . . .

Be assured that evolutionists do see—actually quite clearly, according to Romans 1:20—the purpose of things in nature. But admitting purpose would imply intent, whose source has only been observed from intelligence.

. . . .

respond to concentrations of regulators or protein products. Regulators are activated by "signals" usually sensed by the cell membrane.

Clearly, networks yield abundant combinations with extensive results: from proteins to forming totally different cell types. Broader regulations direct the shapes of diverse organisms from larger (often similar) portions of DNA. And similar networks exist in humans to bacteria. How do evolutionists say they originated?

Network expert Dr. Uri Alon brings enlightenment: "Did network motifs such as FFLs [feedforward loops] evolve in a similar way, in that an ancestral FFL duplicated and gave rise to the present FFLs? In most cases, it seems that the answer is no." That is because, though protein sequences may be similar, "the sequence of the regulators is sometimes so different that they are classed into completely different transcription factor families." So, how is network similarity explained? "It therefore seems that, in many cases, evolution has converged independently on the same

regulation circuit."[4]

So, Gould insists that similar arm bones are explained *only* by common ancestry, but Alon insists that similarities in regulatory networks are *not* due to common ancestry—but "evolution" repeatedly chanced upon it.

It is ironic that Darwin mocked the creationist view (which science may just establish) "that it has pleased the Creator to construct all the animals and plants in each great class on a uniform plan" as "not a scientific explanation,"[5] while his disciples struggle to explain similar features in terms of common ancestry…or not.

Pulling It All Together

People are well able to discern the purpose of a bat's wing, so emphasizing the similar purpose of various organisms' similar features is a natural pushback to evolutionism's implicit atheism. Organisms interacting with environmental properties on the same planet would be expected to share similar features. Research has shown elements in developmental pathways and genetics common to many creatures forming similar structures, yet under an exquisite control that directs them into the applications for each unique kind of creature. These same programs allow remarkable adaptability of most of those structures.

These facts will point people to see how life really operates. Expose evolution's substitute god, natural selection, by showing that "nature" never "selects" or "acts on" organisms, but rather *creatures occupy environments* when the population's inherent adaptability generates traits that fit assorted niches. This *innate* ability is programmed into the entire creature, right from the original creation, enabling it to satisfy the Lord's purpose for His creatures to fill the earth. ●

References
1. Lewontin, R. 1997. Billions and Billions of Demons. *The New York Review of Books.* 44 (1): 31.
2. Gould, S. 1994. Evolution as Fact and Theory. In *Hen's Teeth and Horse's Toes.* New York: W. W. Norton & Company, 253-262.
3. An outstanding resource documenting widespread stasis is Werner, C. 2008. *Living Fossils. Evolution: The Grand Experiment,* vol 2. Green Forest, AR: New Leaf Publishing Group.
4. Alon, U. 2007. Network motifs: theory and experimental approaches. *Nature Reviews Genetics.* 8 (6): 459.
5. Darwin, C. 1872. *The Origin of Species By Means of Natural Selection,* 6th ed. London: John Murray, 383.

A construction contractor struggling to prevent a failed project criticized his designer as "flying by the seat of his pants," meaning that he was simply making up stuff as the project progressed. Projects that lack clearly defined purpose or key design objectives generally fail. Purpose and design are inseparable.[1] Only a foolish architect would propose a project devoid of purpose. So it is astounding how explanations of nature's design by evolutionary theorists—a career field that never designs anything—not only intentionally decouple purpose and design, but are presented as something to boast about.

That thinking by evolutionists was predictable. According to Romans 1, nature's design is so clear, so obvious, and so understandable that people of all ages in all cultures can easily see the Lord's "eternal power and Godhead." The one who actively suppresses this truth becomes a God-denier, an act that leaves him "without excuse."

The Bible adds another valuable insight that is useful in any conversation about the origin of nature's design. Truth suppressors who profess themselves to be wise actually become fools. One certain reality is that evolutionary explanations of nature's design will invariably be foolish—they cannot escape this—and everyone else just needs to be mindful to look.

Is it possible to know where a conversation will end up—without fail—right from the beginning? Yes. This useful assurance will help believers who worry that evolutionists

will produce a "killer" explanation that crushes creationist thinking. *True* evolutionists *must* deny purpose in nature. Since design and purpose are inseparable, they violate this principle at their peril. Just as purposeless construction projects fail, evolutionary thinking forces failed scientific explanations—leaving only incoherent or mystical stories.

The First Step to Incoherence: Deny Nature's Purpose

The Accreditation Board for Engineering and Technology states that "engineering design is the process of devising a system, component, or process to meet desired needs. It is a decision-making process (often iterative), in which the basic science and mathematics and engineering sciences are applied to convert resources optimally to meet a stated objective."[1] The centrality of purpose to design is emphasized twice. Purpose initiates design processes, and designs are constrained to meet the purpose.

Evolutionists choose not to accept nature's purpose since purpose affirms intent, willful decisions, or other attributes of personality, and only God is big enough to implement a purpose for earth. Thus, evolutionists *must* eschew "teleology," the study of purpose in nature. But the purpose-recognition instinct is so strong, biologists struggle to escape it. Evolutionist David Hanke complained:

> Biology is sick. Fundamentally unscientific modes of thought are increasingly accepted....[T]he heart of the problem is

that we persist in making (literally) sense of a world that we know to be senseless by attributing subjective values to the objects in it, values that have no basis in reality.... [I]t is no longer acceptable to think of biological objects as having any purpose because the overwhelming consensus of scientific opinion is that they were not designed and built by a Creator (a mental construct necessary to inject a human sense of purpose into existence) with purposes in mind for them. Instead we believe (I'll put that as strongly as I can) they are products of Darwinian evolution.[2]

For evolutionism, design must somehow arise from mindless properties of matter. The belief that nothing exists outside of matter is called "materialism." Would evolutionists persist in this mindset unfazed, even knowing that excluding purpose is toxic to sensible explanations? It seems so. Evolutionary authority Richard Lewontin is candid about this materialistic implication:

> We have a prior commitment, a commitment to materialism...we are forced by our *a priori* adherence to material causes...that produce material explanations, no matter how counter-intuitive, no matter how mystifying to the uninitiated. Moreover, that materialism is an absolute, for we cannot allow a Divine Foot in the door.[3]

Learning a Short Example

Do evolutionists really maintain explanations that are "counter-intuitive" and "mystifying to the uninitiated"?

The Folly of Design without Purpose

Explaining the universe's origin, cosmologist Stephen Hawking says:

Because there is a law such as gravity, the Universe can and will create itself from nothing. Spontaneous creation is the reason there is something rather than nothing, why the universe exists, why we exist....It is not necessary to invoke God to light the blue touch paper and set the Universe going.[4]

Another theorist detailed why Hawking's views are plausible:

Then there's the idea of inflation, which predicts that an extremely tiny region of space can blow up into a universe-sized domain. Modern cosmologists believe that inflation, once it starts, can keep going forever, continually creating new "pocket universes" with different conditions in each one.[5]

Theoretical physicist Lawrence Krauss adds:

So if we can explain a raindrop, why can't we explain a universe? Mr. Hawking based his argument on the possible existence of extra dimensions—and perhaps an infinite number of universes, which would indeed make the spontaneous appearance of a universe like ours seem almost trivial.[6]

In biology, the National Academy of Sciences solved the origins dilemma for how molecular machines got all of their parts at the right time and place:

We proposed that simple "core" machines were established in the first eukaryotes by drawing on pre-existing bacterial proteins that had previously provided distinct functions. Subsequently, and in a stepwise process in keeping with Darwinian evolution, additional modules would have been added to the core machines to enhance their function.[7]

Evolutionist Kathryn Applegate of BioLogos joins in: "The bacterial flagellum may look like an outboard motor, but there is at least one profound difference: the flagellum assembles spontaneously, without the help of any conscious agent." Acknowledging that "the self-assembly of such a complex machine almost defies the imagination," she justifies shrugging off this difficulty since "natural forces work 'like magic.'"[8]

Then there's natural selection's clever abilities to evolve systems: "The discovery that the hemoglobins of jawed and jawless vertebrates were invented independently provides powerful testimony to the ability of natural selection to cobble together similar design solutions using different starting materials."[9] Or how humans inherited basic parts of their nervous system from sponges: "'Evolution can take these "off-the-shelf" components and put them together in new and interesting ways,' said study leader Kenneth Kosik....Other genes would also have had to evolve or to have been co-opted to create complex nervous systems, such as our own."[10]

Just as purposeless construction projects fail, evolutionary thinking forces failed scientific explanations—leaving only incoherent or mystical stories.

After studying a pivotal fossil, Britain's top science journal explained its evolutionary ancestry:

This forces us to infer much longer ghost lineages for tetrapods and elpistostegids [lobe-finned fish] than the body fossil record suggests....(Ghost lineages are those that must have existed at a particular time, according to the phylogeny, but which are not represented by fossils at that time.)[11]

What about humans? In jocular evolutionary speculation, Oliver Curry expects future genetic-based classes of humans will emerge:

People would become choosier about their sexual partners, causing humanity to divide into sub-species....The descendants of the genetic upper class would be tall, slim, healthy, attractive, intelligent, and creative and a far cry from the "underclass" humans who would have evolved into dim-witted, ugly, squat goblin-like creatures.[12]

Evolutionary theorists appear to build one incoherent or mysterious explanation upon another—an "uninitiated" contractor might be tempted to conclude that they are flying by the seat of their pants.

Pulling It All Together

The best explanation for design remains the main issue. Is it real or only apparent? True evolutionary explanations for apparent design must separate two things that cannot be disconnected: purpose and design.

Should Christians feel threatened by a foolish worldview that inevitably produces counterintuitive explanations that appeal to an infinitude of self-creating universes where an unobserved force—natural selection—co-opts discrete, off-the-shelf molecular parts and cobbles together complex machines that self-assemble like magic, eventually emerging, after a long trail of ghost lineages, as organisms which, by the year 3000, will give rise to dim-witted goblins coexisting with their cousins—genetically superior attractive humans?

"Why don't you believe in evolution?" A totally rational response is: "Explanations that assert that the diversity of life on earth is the outcome of a blind purposeless process are ridiculous. I have no desire to engage in self-delusion that the exquisite features of design seen in nature are all an illusion. A far better explanation is that the Lord Jesus Christ created each kind of organism with inherent capabilities to diversify in order to fill environments on the earth...which they do remarkably well." ◉

References

1. ABET Definition of Design. The University of Nevada, Las Vegas. Posted on me.unlv.edu, accessed October 8, 2010.
2. Hanke, D. 2004. Teleology: The explanation that bedevils biology. In *Explanations: Styles of explanation in science*. Cornwell, J., ed. New York: Oxford University Press, 143-155.
3. Lewontin, R. 1997. Billions and Billions of Demons. *The New York Review of Books*. 44 (1): 31.
4. Roberts, L. Stephen Hawking: God was not needed to create the Universe. *Telegraph*. Posted on telegraph.co.uk September 2, 2010, accessed October 8, 2010.
5. Carroll, S. The 'Why?' Questions, Chapter and Multiverse. *Wall Street Journal*. Posted on online.wsj.com September 24, 2010, accessed October 8, 2010.
6. Krauss, L. M. Our Spontaneous Universe. *Wall Street Journal*. Posted on online.wsj.com September 8, 2010, accessed October 8, 2010.
7. Clements, A. et al. 2009. The reducible complexity of a mitochondrial molecular machine. *Proceedings of the National Academy of Sciences*. 106 (37):15791-15795.
8. Applegate, K. Self-Assembly of the Bacterial Flagellum: No Intelligence Required. The BioLogos Forum. Posted on biologos.org August 19, 2010, accessed October 8, 2010.
9. Simons, T. Biologists find that red-blooded vertebrates evolved twice, independently. University of Nebraska-Lincoln news release, July 26, 2010.
10. Than, K. Origins of Human Nervous System Found in Sea Sponges. *LiveScience*. Posted on livescience.com June 6, 2007, accessed October 8, 2010.
11. Niedźwiedzki, G. et al. 2010. Tetrapod trackways from the early Middle Devonian period of Poland. *Nature*. 463 (7277): 43-48.
12. Human species 'may split in two.' *BBC News*. Posted on news.bbc.co.uk October 17, 2006, accessed October 8, 2010.

Evaluating Real vs. Apparent Design

Everyone has some unhealthy habits and the best way to achieve long-term freedom from them is not to "drop" them but to "replace" them with something better. The freedom-through-replacement reality is also useful during any conversation about evolution's failure to explain the origin of nature's design, since, at some point, an evolutionist is likely to ask, "Well, do you propose something better?"

Creationists, in fact, do have a scientifically better explanation to replace the notion that nature's design is all an illusion that stems from a purposeless process in which evolution's substitute god, the imaginary "Natural Selector,"[1] chooses the fittest mutations randomly arising in an organism's DNA. A concise answer could be, "Our claim that nature's design is produced by a real designer can be tested by observation and is mathematically quantifiable. Furthermore, compared to the legacy of evolutionary thinking, it liberates minds to pursue more rational approaches toward scientific research."

That answer ought to catch attention and keep discussion on the main question: "What is the best explanation of nature's design?" The Bible says in Romans 1:18-23 that the Lord's witness to His reality is "clearly seen" from the "creation" by the things He has "made." He used the language of design construction, not biology. Everyone can see nature's design and conclude it was designed—by a cause bigger than

nature. Thus, Romans details how everyone's accountability to acknowledge God has always been based on the very clear design-designer (i.e., created-creator) connection, demonstrated by all human cultures, and not on detailed biological insight.

So, the biological question "how do organisms adapt to environments?" is not the root issue, which is founded on a basic question corresponding to problem-solving activities of intelligent engineers:

Are features of design evident when the *innate programming* of organisms actively *solves problems* (or exploits opportunities) presented by environments?

Real Design: A Scientifically Superior Explanation

Begin by stating that you have carefully examined the two explanations head-to-head. You find the explanation for real design is more persuasive since the activities of real engineers—which cannot be duplicated by natural processes—are reflected in the living world. Then, enumerate four verifiable *observations* that reflect real design.

Possibly the clearest observation of organisms is that they have multiple intricately arranged parts that fit together for a purpose. Many of these parts show proper alignment, exact dimensions and shape, tight fit, proper balance, and moving parts with precisely synchronized timing. These *complex* patterns are

features of design that have been observed to originate only in intelligently designed items— never by natural forces.

One fact about sections of DNA is that their four letters are precisely arranged as a set of plans and specification detailing the materials and controls to reproduce a new organism. Since DNA 1) selects 2) in advance 3) exact attributes 4) for a purpose, it has the same features of intelligence as any engineer's specification. Throughout recorded human experience, plans and specifications are always a product of intelligence. In addition, all known natural processes that randomly choose letters one-by-one outside the context of an intelligence to guide the selection—as evolutionists assert—always yield *nonsense* that is totally inconsistent with information held in DNA.

Another certain feature of design is demonstrated when engineers *foresee* aspects of their project that cannot be built by increments. They respond by establishing conditions so all information and materials are 1) available, 2) localized together, 3) at the right time, 4) capable of functioning together 5) for the intended purpose. Only intelligent agents have been observed to set conditions where *all* of the parts must be collected and built together or *none* of a specific function is obtained. Creatures have many examples of this *all-or-nothing* unity, but the best example is reproduction. Evolution is a dead end without operative reproductive abilities. Intelligent foresight best explains why the

minimum number of parts necessary for an organism to reproduce—is the organism itself.

Mathematicians have quantified the probability of the information for the most basic functional proteins developing by natural processes as exceedingly small.[2] Therefore, it is not a stretch to assert that it is mathematically impossible to obtain by natural processes the information that is needed for the origin of a living, reproducing bacterium. Overcoming infinitesimally small probabilities in a single bound by engaging them—as evolutionists do—with infinite numbers of resources generated by an infinite number of universes falls outside the realm of acceptable scientific explanations.

Intricately arranged parts, information for specifications, all-or-nothing unity, and the impossibly low probabilities of these things happening in living things by chance are *real* observations. Their association to the actions of real designers is visible. Science is based on observation and testing. Real design is the better scientific explanation.

A better scientific explanation supports a better approach to science. Since these features point so clearly toward real design, biological researchers should approach investigations of nature like engineers would study an unknown electronic device. They should expect to discover well-designed, coherent, and incredibly complex systems functioning for a purpose—an expectation forbidden by the rules governing evolution's mental "thought prison."

Escaping the Thought Prison Called "Apparent Design"

Being confined to a tiny cell is the depressing reality that makes prison awful. But even worse is when a mind is so straitjacketed by the atheistic philosophy of naturalism that it eagerly believes explanations that are *resisted* by scientific observations. Claiming that the purpose of an eagle's wing cannot be known and that the synchronized movement of all its precisely fitted parts is only an "illusion of design" is a perception contrary to real external stimuli. How much better could scientists—set free to conclude design when they see design—approach research when released from miscon-

ceptions that flow from invalid, yet firmly held, reasoning constricted by naturalism?

First, researchers would be free to follow data wherever it leads, which allows them to never stop questioning and discovering. This mental state far exceeds the shackled thinking characterized by a candid statement from a Kansas State University professor:

> Even if all of the data point to an intelligent designer, such a hypothesis is excluded from science because it is not naturalistic. Of course the scientist, as an individual, is free to embrace a reality that transcends naturalism.[3]

Second, there is freedom from the sense-dulling obligatory conclusion that intricate designs are "only an illusion"—a peer-enforced mantra indistinguishable from forced indoctrination. Researchers would not be pressured by popular evolutionary authorities such as

> The explanation for real design is more persuasive since the activities of real engineers—which cannot be duplicated by natural processes—are reflected in the living world.

Cambridge's Richard Dawkins, who insists that "biology is the study of complicated things that have the appearance of having been designed for a purpose."[4] Or by Francis Crick, a co-discoverer of DNA, who cautioned, "Biologists must constantly keep in mind that what they see was not designed, but rather evolved."[5]

Third, it would liberate researchers from a smothering presupposition that *expects* regular mistakes in nature due to millions of years of chaotic evolution. They will escape a blinding mindset inclined to label not-readily-defined findings as "junk," "vestigial," or "bad design." Reacting to observations with ill-informed hasty conclusions such as labeling non-protein-coding DNA "junk DNA" or the human appendix a "vestigial organ" is not only poor scientific practice, but this prejudice tends toward neglect in research. Stanford University reported on immunological research on "natural killer" cells that "have largely been ignored

by immunologists…[and] thought by some to be an archaic remnant of the primitive mammalian immune system."[6]

Pulling It All Together

In a conversation about the best explanation for the origin of nature's design, first expose the weakness of the assertion that design is "only an illusion." Recount how evolutionists rely on a mindless iterative process to accumulate genetic mistakes "favored" by totally imaginary forces from their stand-in god, natural selection. The impotence of this mechanism always forces them to make conclusions far exceeding what the data support. Consequently, they resort to "counter-intuitive" scenarios that are "mystifying to the uninitiated," full of infinite numbers of self-creating universes where microscopic biological machines "self assemble" by "co-opting" "off the shelf parts," leading to creatures with "ghost lineages" that magically "arise" or "burst onto the scene." So even if the evolutionist doesn't ask "can you offer something better?"…do it anyway.

Creationists can show that nature's design has features associated with those known *only* to be derived from real designers. Support is based on *actual* observations of living things' intricately arranged parts, plans and specifications reflected in DNA's information, and many examples of all-or-nothing unity. This truth frees researchers to expect that nature is a product of a rational, coherent design, a path that will lead to research that is once again open to fresh insights into nature. In biology, discovering purposes is better than forcing the absurdity that purpose is unknowable. Real design is the better scientific explanation, and free minds are better than imprisoned minds. ◉

References
1. Hanke, D. 2004. Teleology: The explanation that bedevils biology. In *Explanations: Styles of explanation in science*. Cornwell, J., ed. New York: Oxford University Press, 143-155.
2. Axe, D. 2004. Estimating the prevalence of protein sequences adopting functional enzyme folds. *Journal of Molecular Biology*. 341 (5): 1295-1315.
3. Todd, S. C. 1999. A view from Kansas on that evolution debate. *Nature*. 401 (6752): 423.
4. Dawkins, R. 1986. *The Blind Watchmaker*. London: WW Norton & Company, 1.
5. Crick, F. 1988. *What Mad Pursuit: A Personal View of Scientific Discovery*. London: Sloan Foundation Science, 138.
6. Weidenbach, K. Natural-born killers: An immunologic enigma solved. *Stanford Report*. Stanford University news release, January 14, 1998.

Life's Optimized Design Mirrors Its Perfect Creator

Winning the "concrete canoe" contest amongst various college schools of engineering is tough. One design constraint is that Portland cement, a key component of concrete, must be used to build a multi-person craft. Engineering students strive to achieve the best balance between competing functional needs. In the end, their optimized canoe designs are amazingly strong, light, and polished, and press the properties of cement to their known limits. Contests like these force students to find the finest balance of seemingly contradictory demands, and are taken as one measure of each engineering school's intellectual and technical prowess.

The ability to choose the best words or actions to satisfy competing interests in any situation is a mark of wisdom as well as intelligence. The Bible describes how the Lord Jesus Christ always found the perfect answer in response to people with questions designed to entrap Him in a philosophical dilemma. For example, how does one resolve the demands of perfect justice and perfect mercy for a woman shown as an adulteress? Jesus said, "He that is without sin among you, let him first cast a stone at her" (John 8:7).

It should, therefore, not be surprising that the Lord's designs in creation are characterized by a wise, optimal blend of features: "O LORD, how manifold are thy works! in wisdom hast thou made them all" (Psalm 104:24). A reasonable prediction flowing from this truth is that researchers should "clearly see" evidences of *optimized* design in living things as they fit into their environments.

What Is Optimized Design?

Achieving an optimized design is an extremely difficult challenge for engineers, since it means they must satisfy competing needs-based design requirements to obtain the best balance of solved problems within the limits of current technological capabilities. At times, competing interests can be so intense they contradict each other (e.g., versatility versus simplicity). When the end product's performance cannot get any better at meeting all needs within the constraints of current technology, it is said to have achieved the "optimized design."

Why is it so difficult to design optimized systems or products? The answer lies in the factors that constrain the design. First, it is difficult to know what all of these factors are. All constraints need to be explored to understand how they function, and some may even need to be discovered. Second, hard choices need to be made to prioritize the solutions to the constraints for any given situation. Since each individual interest's solution may not be the best that it "selfishly" could be, there is always some "tradeoffs" with other interests. Finally, it is very difficult from a constructability standpoint to balance solutions to the many competing interests. A high-priority interest may turn out to be far more difficult or expensive to build than a lower-priority interest—which forces difficult rounds of re-prioritization.

Words often used in technical literature for optimized designs are "balanced proportions," "good economy," "layering," "redundancy," "minimized cost of errors," and "finely tuned overall operation." Using these words in conversation is certain to resonate with true design in the minds of listeners.

Optimized Features Are Always Evidence of Intelligence

Why is finding optimally designed things a certain sign of intelligent activity or one thing, in situations where the original source of optimized design is truly known, it has always come from an intelligent source. Nonliving natural phenomena such as raw energy from the sun, wind, gravity, precipitation, and such, cannot produce real designs. Evolutionists always want to use the designed information and parts *already* innate to living things as proof they somehow originated naturally—"it exists because natural selection favored it"—but this is cheating.

The other reason is in the tradeoffs themselves. Far from showing poor design, tradeoffs are a characteristic of good design. In either case, tradeoffs show true design. They are always the outcome of a choice-making ability that, again, in all of human experience has an intelligent source.

Evolutionists Appeal to Mystical Explanations for Optimized Biological Design

The fact that many features of living things show optimized design is evident to researchers, especially biophysicists. One researcher from the Salk Institute said that the eye's retinal function "may sample the visual scene with high precision, perhaps in a manner that approaches the optimum for high-resolution vision."[1]

In yet another example, a leading researcher of bone structure from MIT discussed the fine balance of properties of bone's major component, collagen. He said, "The risk of catastrophic brittle-like failure needs to be minimized to sustain optimal biological function….In addition to optimization for mechanical properties, other design objectives, such as biological function, chemical properties, or functional constraints, may be responsible for the structure of collagen."[2] In spite of the fact that collagen's structure meets multiple "design objectives," this evolutionist mysteriously credits "Nature" with achieving this objective.

In a report in *Science* on how humans could benefit in adaptive network development by copying the optimized abilities of slime mold, the researchers claimed, "Unlike anthropogenic infrastructure systems, these biological networks have been subjected to successive rounds of evolutionary selection and are likely to have reached a point at which cost, efficiency, and resilience are appropriately balanced." In addition to balancing the needs of cost, efficiency, and breakdown-resistance better than man-made systems, slime mold networks also "develop without centralized control and may represent a readily scalable solution for growing networks in general."[3] Given the extraordinary design under their examination, only a prior bias against the most likely explanation of optimization—intelligent design—could explain the unintelligible transfer of credit to an unconscious mental construct like "evolutionary selection."

> Optimization is just another evidence of design in the living world that *resists* being explained by natural causes.

Learning a Short Example

On other occasions, evolutionary biologists brazenly criticize highly complicated biological systems as "poorly designed." Could there be a better explanation? Even if a creationist did not know all of the technical details underlying the design of the human eye, he could still give a great response based on the principles of optimized design. A conversation may be started, for example, with someone who parrots evolutionary biologist Frank Zindler's assertion that the human retina is "put together backwards." He claimed, "Although the human eye would be a scandal if it were the result of divine deliberation, a plausible evolutionary explanation of its absurd construction can be obtained quite easily [from evolutionary trial-and-error]."[4]

Start your rebuttal of this by pointing out that arguments of "bad design" are really assertions from ignorance. Not that Mr. Zindler is unintelligent, but he may be ignorant, from a design perspective, of the need to balance several competing interests in order to obtain an optimized design. Unless all needs are known—which, currently, they are not— no one can argue as to why the human retina or anything else is poor design. Zindler may be ignorant of known good reasons for design tradeoffs between various traits, and other reasons may yet be discovered. Design tradeoffs are actually a better indicator of intelligence behind a design.

The fact that a design doesn't maximize performance of the one particular trait capturing Zindler's interest is irrelevant as to whether the entity as a whole was truly designed. He should know that quality, in itself, is never an indicator of design, since many human-designed items are truly poorly designed. Ask the Zindler fan, "Do you really believe the human eye is poorly designed given that no human-constructed sensor of any type comes even remotely near its performance?"

Pulling It All Together

Achieving an optimized design is an extraordinary challenge for intelligent engineers struggling to satisfy competing needs-based design requirements. Optimization is just another evidence of design in the living world that *resists* being explained by natural causes. Since criticisms against great optimized designs such as the human eye[5] have been shown to be arguments from ignorance, there is no reason a person should believe that living creatures only look like they were designed…but weren't.

In contrast, choosing the best actions to satisfy competing interests and to execute them in complex systems in any situation is a mark of both wisdom and intelligence. The testimony of this world's abundant intricately optimized biological designs is that the Lord Jesus Christ demonstrates surpassing excellence at both! ●

References
1. How the retina works: Like a multi-layered jigsaw puzzle of receptive fields. Salk Institute for Biological Studies news release. Posted on salk.edu April 7, 2009, accessed July 20, 2012.
2. Buehler, M. J. 2006. Nature designs tough collagen: Explaining the nanostructure of collagen fibrils. *Proceedings of the National Academy of Sciences*. 103 (33): 12285-12290.
3. Tero, A. et al. 2010. Rules for Biologically Inspired Adaptive Network Design. *Science*. 327 (5964): 439-442.
4. Does an objective look at the human eye show evidence of creation? Posted on 2think.org, accessed July 26, 2012.
5. The accompanying questions and answers have more information on the design of the human eye. See also Bergman, J. and J. Calkins. 2005. Is the Backwards Human Retina Evidence of Poor Design? *Acts & Facts*. 34 (10).

A recent political argument raged over who should get credit for building the infrastructure that sustains American business. No matter where one stands on who really "built it," everyone knows that it did not build itself. Yet when it comes to the origination of life's extraordinarily more complex infrastructure, evolutionists insist that the exquisite fit of creatures to their environment somehow built itself. Why would anyone believe something so counterintuitive?

The answer has nothing to do with science and everything to do with a person's desire to be self-ruled. If someone doesn't want to be accountable to the Creator, they can try to explain Him away…something hard to accomplish at any time. Why? In all human cultures, people know that things do not make themselves. When people look at themselves, they can clearly see that they look made. Therefore, they must have a Maker.

Everyone can see nature's design and conclude it was designed by a cause bigger than nature. As stated in an earlier chapter, Romans 1:18-22 indicates that everyone's accountability to acknowledge God's existence has always been based on a very clear design-designer (i.e., created-creator) connection. In fact, nature's design is so clear, so obvious, and so understandable that people can actually see the Lord's "eternal power and Godhead." Not only can they see that God exists, but far more importantly, God as Creator actually declares who God *is*.

Astoundingly, when creationists teach on why the Genesis creation account is relevant to Christians, they invariably focus on abortion, family breakups, school violence, pornography, racism, or homosexual behavior. While these are important, they do not even come close to capturing the monumental importance of creation to the Christian faith. Even the fact of the original sin of "the first man Adam" explaining why humanity needed "the last Adam" as the Savior is not the most relevant reason to uphold the reality of the creation account.

The link of the creation event to the reality of a Creator God is the supreme reason why "in the beginning *God created* the heaven and the earth"[1] ultimately matters.

The Doctrine of God Is Based on Creation

"What is God like?" is a significant question. However, "who *is* God?" is possibly the most important question. Christians generally assert that God is the Creator. But a very biblical way to accurately focus understanding is to say that the Creator of all things *is* God. The *cause* of the creation of all things is the way God has chosen to identify Himself—which is why the Bible begins with "in the beginning God created."

In a very real sense, the very name "God" designates a position of rank or status of One who surpasses everything. The way that we conceive of the highest being is by reckoning that He is the ultimate source—or cause—of everything. All things owe their created existence to and are dependent on Him. So, the reality of the ultimate "effect," the creation of the universe itself, is fundamentally necessary to establish the ultimate cause—namely, the reality of God.

This reality denotes certain God-specific (or, from our perspective, God-defining) attributes such as self-existent, self-active, eternal, and unlimited, which are independent of the existence of moral attributes like holiness or love. An all-powerful creator of all things would still be "God" even if it delighted in torturing its creation. We can be exceedingly

Life's Created Design and the Doctrine of God

thankful that the true Creator God is actually unlimited in perfect love.

The creation account in Genesis, in which God calls into existence time, space, and matter, is a succinct, matter-of-fact statement. It is similarly repeated throughout the Bible, such as in Psalm 33:6: "By the word of the LORD were the heavens made; and all the host of them by the breath of his mouth." Yet, this truth immediately establishes the fact that matter is neither eternal nor does it self-develop—thus ruling out popular false notions posited by secular scholars today.

Christian faith has always recognized the basic union of the doctrines of creation and God, which is missed by some present-day Christians who readily forsake the doctrine of creation when attacked by cynics. As early as 325 A.D. at the First Council of Nicaea, Christian leaders used biblical truth to correct false teachings about God. Their doctrinal statement intended to be memorized by Christians, the Creed of Caesarea, clearly defines God foremost as the sovereign Creator:

> We believe in one God, the Father All-sovereign, the maker of things visible and invisible; And in one Lord Jesus Christ, the Word of God, God of God, Light of Light, Life of Life, Son only-begotten, Firstborn of all creation, begotten of the Father before all the ages, through whom also all things were made; who was made flesh for our salvation.[2]

Today, many churches still trace their doctrine about God to several biblically based affirmations flowing from Reformation events. Two great statements, the Westminster Confession of Faith (1646) and the Baptist Confession of Faith (1689), begin by linking the triune God with the creation.

> In the beginning it pleased God the Father, Son, and Holy Spirit, for the manifestation of the glory of His eternal power, wisdom, and goodness, to create or make the world and all things in it both visible and invisible, in the space of six days, and all very good.[3]

The intricacies of life's design that clearly look so intelligently crafted will prompt people to seek to explain their cause. Who is their Creator? The Bible says the Creator is God…but it reveals even more.

The Lord Jesus Christ Is the Intelligent Designer

Since the Creator of everything is God, then the Lord Jesus Christ is Himself God, since the Bible identifies Him as the Creator. John 1:1-3 makes the creator-deity link of Jesus:

> In the beginning was the Word, and the Word was with God, and the Word was God. The same was in the beginning with God. All things were made by him; and without him was not any thing made that was made.

Note in Colossians 1:16-17 that not only is the creating power of Jesus Christ recognized, but His sustaining capacity as well:

> For by him were all things created, that are in heaven, and that are in earth, visible and invisible, whether they be thrones, or dominions, or principalities, or powers: all things were created by him, and for him: And he is before all things, and by him all things consist.

The link of the creation event to the reality of a Creator God is the supreme reason why "in the beginning *God created* the heaven and the earth" ultimately matters.

That is why Colossians 2:9 can encapsulate Jesus as the incarnation of God: "For in him dwelleth all the fulness of the Godhead bodily."

Again, in Hebrews 1:2-3 the Lord Jesus as God the Son is described as the express image of God the Father, who "hath in these last days spoken unto us by his Son, whom he hath appointed heir of all things, by whom also he made the worlds; Who being the brightness of his glory, and the express image of his person, and upholding all things by the word of his power…"

Learning a Short Example

Are evolutionary thinkers perceptive enough to ascertain the link between life's created design and the very doctrine of God? Would that link be shrewdly cut by cleverly substituting an idolatrous mystical force spe-

cifically to explain life's design? Would this explanation be considered a plausible reason not to believe in God? It seems so. Consider this summation by evolutionary authority Daniel Dennett:

> With evolution, however, it is different. The fundamental scientific idea of evolution by natural selection is not just mind-boggling; natural selection, by executing God's traditional task of designing and creating all creatures great and small, also seems to deny one of the best reasons we have for believing in God.[4]

Pulling It All Together

Scientists appreciate an elegant explanation that uses simple principles to elucidate perplexing observations. To demonstrate to people that an extraordinary Creator exists, what could be more simple and yet profound than to appeal to universal human creative activities in which created things always have a creator, and then set stunning examples of creation that they themselves can observe—life's phenomenal intricate designs? At the root level for everyone, people can know that they are an effect that must have a cause. That cause *is* God.

For Christians, the reason why the Creator of all things is God should be implicitly relevant: They are theists. Astute atheistic evolutionists know this. While they cannot disprove God, they can create a social climate that intimidates Christians who fear others' opinions into disowning "in the beginning God created." In terms of the doctrine of creation, for Christians to abandon, ignore, minimalize, fail to defend, or subjugate its relevance to social issues is tantamount to plunging a knife into their spiritual abdomens. It is spiritual suicide for theists to forsake the doctrine of creation, because it is the basis for the very doctrine of who God is—the Creator of everything. ◉

References
1. Genesis 1:1, emphasis added.
2. Bettenson, H. S. 1963. *Documents of the Christian Church.* New York: Oxford University Press, 24.
3. The Westminster Confession adds the words "of nothing" after "world."
4. Dennett, D. C. Show Me the Science. *The New York Times*, August 28, 2005.

FOR FURTHER STUDY

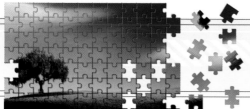

Fit & Function: Design in Nature

Questions

1. Consider the scientific dispute over the two predominant views of the origin of the universe: Could the universe have created itself out of nothing, or did it need to be created by something outside of itself? From a biblical understanding, how important is the origin of the universe to our understanding of who God is?

_____

_____

_____

2. How does the Bible support the idea that understanding design helps others to have a proper *initial* understanding of God? Did God actually start the "intelligent design" argument as evidence for His existence?

_____

_____

_____

3. A powerful and important argument for God's existence can be made by looking for two basic features in living things that are similar to man-made things. What are those features, and why do they show design?

_____

_____

_____

4. What are the two different explanations offered by creationists and evolutionists for the origination of design in living things?

_____

_____

_____

Answers

1. The Bible makes abundantly clear that God is first and foremost the Creator, stating, "In the beginning God created the heaven and the earth" (Genesis 1:1). All things owe their very existence to God, but He owes nothing to, and needs nothing from, anything He has created.

2. The Bible indicates that people can know there is a Creator by understanding the things He has made. Romans 1:19-20 says, "That which may be known of God is manifest in them [those who deny God]: for God hath shewed it unto them. For the invisible things of him from the creation of the world are clearly seen, being understood by the things that are made, even his eternal power and Godhead; so they are without excuse." God Himself, the Author of Scripture, seems to have been the first to use the obvious fact of design as evidence for His existence. The things He has made, primarily the living things, reveal a Creator because they bear many of the same features as man-made things. Everyone can see that created things have a creator and that created things do not create themselves.

3. All design starts with identifying a need, which is the *purpose* for starting the design. The purpose constrains the design, even leading to design modifications as the purpose becomes clearer or changes. Random natural forces cannot be expected to bring about things that function for a purpose. Thus, purpose is usually a clear sign of intelligent action.

   Along the same line of thought, when things match or complement each other—in other words, when they *fit* together—it is not only a sign of intelligence, it is usually the result of hard work. Thus, when things fit, an action intrinsic to design, a clear-cut mental impression of intelligence is made.

4. Creationists explain the genuine design seen in nature as flowing from a real Designer. This is the naturally favored reason in the minds of people, since it is consistent with all human experience. Materialists—those who believe that the laws of nature and matter alone are operative in nature—claim that there is no designer and that the design clearly seen by everyone is a false impression. Since that explanation goes against all of human experience when it comes to the origination of a design, this is a tough sell for evolutionists.

   A creationist has a big advantage when talking about design because everyone sees the design in living things! You can rest assured that when the Bible says that the design is "clearly seen," in fact, it is. There is no need to wonder if someone sees the design in a bird that is fit to fly.

Unmasking Evolution's Magic Words

Questions

1. Why would a scientist not consider all possible explanations about how living things operate and how they originated? Why do evolutionary scientists appeal to "magic words" in their explanations?

   _____

   _____

   _____

2. Can you recall hearing any other magic words that were not in included the article? How could you improve your skills at spotting magic words?

   _____

   _____

   _____

3. What are some ways to educate others about the use of magic words in evolutionary explanations? Why do such words weaken those explanations?

   _____

   _____

   _____

Answers

1. Most evolutionists are materialists and are thus compelled by their philosophical ideology to search for only natural explanations to explain the biological world. However, this forces them to use "magic words," since:

    1) There is no experimental evidence that life can arise from non-living molecules.

    2) There is not one observable instance in which descendants of one creature have ever been seen to slowly change over many generations into a fundamentally different type of creature.

    3) There is no hard fossil evidence documenting a smooth, slow transition of one life form into another as predicted by the evolutionary theory. Instead, all the major body plans suddenly appear in the fossil record, discontinuous from each other.

    Saying that a creature simply "evolved" is a purely mystical explanation and invokes unseen powers. Evolutionary problems are routinely solved in the scientific journals and TV programs by an *ad hoc* assertion that it "just happened," without showing scientifically *how* it happened. But as in all appeals to magic, the connections are mental fantasies not grounded in reality.

2. Other magic words often found in evolutionary journals are "evolution drove," "the early results of...," and "saw the genesis of...." Try to memorize the first five words listed in the article and listen for them on TV programs and look for them in textbooks. Young people can play a game in which they memorize the most common magic words and then compete with each other during a TV program on evolution to see who can spot the first magic word. Part of the game could involve adding up all of the different types of magic words featured in a single program and how many times they were used. Some words used in the program might not be listed in the article, but they could be just as magical.

3. Point out that *ad hoc* claims that something evolved don't even come close to showing scientifically *how* it evolved. This evolutionary ploy is used all the time and people rarely call evolutionists to scientific account. Help others understand that historical science—in which a researcher constructs a story to explain past events—is not the same type of science that puts a man on the moon or devises ways to cure disease. Engineers, medical doctors, and other scientists who rely on studies or experiments do not use magic words.

    Encourage your friends to reject the use of magic words that are the bread-and-butter of the best evolutionary scientific literature. The "Learning a Short Example" scenarios in this book can be an effective tool to draw out details of complexity and make it mentally difficult for anyone to leap over the tall scientific hurdles of explaining how the complexity of living creatures originated through natural processes alone.

Natural Selection Is Not "Nature's Design Process"

Questions

1. Is it accurate to use the words "natural" and "selection" in describing the interactions between an organism and its environment?

_____

_____

2. Is natural selection a process, a force, a concept, or none of these things? How would you define natural selection?

_____

_____

3. How important is natural selection to Darwin's theory?

_____

_____

4. The article identified how there was no actual intelligence in nature that could "select" for any traits. Compare artificial selection to natural selection. Is it possible that natural selection exists only as an idea?

_____

_____

Answers

1. The words "natural" and "selection" do not accurately describe observable interactions between an organism and its environment. People know that to "select" something is presumptive evidence of volition—a special *choice-making* capacity implicit in intelligence. However, nature does not have a brain and possesses no innate intelligence, and therefore cannot "select." The term "natural selection" has been effectively employed to divert attention from where the power to solve environmental problems really resides—strictly within the well-designed innate capabilities of organisms. Natural selection is a mental perception that is not grounded on reality.

2. If you survey research documents, it would be hard to find a consensus definition for natural selection. It may not be definable. In a single paper, some sentences use natural selection as a cause and others use it as an effect. Some authorities say it is only a process, or a law, mechanism, or concept. A British expert on natural selection states the problem concisely:

A quite general issue has still received no canonical treatment: what kind of a thing is natural selection anyway? A law, a principle, a force, a cause, an agent, or all or some of these things? The view that natural selection is a law has been countered by the view that it is a principle, while that conclusion has been countered in turn by an insistence that it is neither."[1]

3. Natural selection is absolutely indispensable to Darwinian evolution. "Nature selects" is the heart of evolution, as exemplified by a few statements from leading Darwinists.

> Daniel Dennett of Tufts University said, "If I were to give an award for the single best idea anyone has ever had, I'd give it to Darwin, ahead of Newton and Einstein and everyone else. In a single stroke, the idea of evolution by natural selection unifies the realm of life, meaning and purpose with the realm of space and time, cause and effect, mechanism and physical law."[2]

> With evolution, however, it is different. The fundamental scientific idea of evolution by natural selection is not just mind-boggling; natural selection, by executing God's traditional task of designing and creating all creatures great and small, also seems to deny one of the best reasons we have for believing in God….The idea that natural selection has the power to generate such sophisticated designs is deeply counterintuitive.[3]

> Stuart Kauffman explained, "Biologists now tend to believe profoundly that natural selection is the invisible hand that crafts well-wrought forms. It may be an overstatement to claim that biologists view selection as the sole source of order in biology, but not by much. If current biology has a central canon, you have now heard it."[4]

4. "Nature" doesn't literally think, yet most organisms' features seem perfectly designed—how could a human brain reconcile those incongruent facts? Darwin drew a false analogy between artificial selection (guided by human intelligence) and natural selection to make the connection. Natural selection carries the evolutionist's explanation for "apparent design." For Darwin, it was easier to see external environments as the causal force acting on organisms, since scientists living then were ignorant of DNA and internal operating cellular machinery. Creatures do fit their environments very well and environmental elements can be seen, so it was thought likely that some type of environmental force caused these remarkably suited adaptations.

References
1. Hodge, M. J. S. 1992. Natural Selection: Historical Perspectives. *Keywords in Evolutionary Biology*. Cambridge, MA: Harvard University Press, 218.
2. Dennett, D. 1995. *Darwin's Dangerous Idea*. New York: Touchstone, 21.
3. Dennett, D. Show Me the Science. *New York Times*, August 28, 2005.
4. Kauffman, S. 1995. *At Home in the Universe: The Search for the Laws of Self-Organization and Complexity*. New York: Oxford University Press, 150. See also Guliuzza, R. 2011. Darwin's Sacred Imposter: How Natural Selection Is Given Credit for Design in Nature. *Acts and Facts*. 40 (7): 12-15.

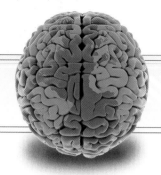

Natural Selection Is Not "Nature's Intelligence"

Questions

1. If natural selection is a process, what are the steps in the process, and how do they differ from the natural outworking of an organism's own innate capabilities?

_____

_____

_____

2. Some have said that the most important fact to identify is where the power for adaptation resides. Why would it be important to precisely determine the source of adaptive power?

_____

_____

_____

3. If natural selection is nothing more than a mystical mental construct, is there a more scientifically accurate and biblically consistent explanation for adaptation?

_____

_____

_____

Answers

1. Advocates of process *always* include three necessary conditions: 1) reproduction of traits 2) which differ in ability to solve environmental problems 3) and which are heritable.[1] The conditions specified to be environmental "selection" (reproduction of variable heritable traits) are in reality the unfolding of genetic abilities programmed into the *organisms themselves*.

2. The source of adaptive power marks a key difference between evolutionary and creationist explanations for life's diversity. Is adaptation an externally driven process as advocated by Darwin and most leading evolutionists? Or could it be an organism-driven process that is actually the outworking of well-regulated internal mechanisms programmed into creatures by the Lord? Note how the steps in the process of natural selection are always defined in terms of the actual outworking of an organism's *own* innate capacities.

   Consider what is left of Darwin's theory on the origin of species by means of natural selection when it is exposed that nothing really exists as an *external force* pressuring populations of organisms and driving evolutionary change. What alternative evolutionary mechanism is seriously being advanced with the potential to explain nature's design other than environments that are somehow capable of selecting inhabitants characterized as the "fittest"?

3. An organism-based, design-based approach to adaptation opens a new and better way to understand what happens. What if it is really *the organism* that is operative with its capacity to reproduce variable heritable traits that are capable of solving environmental problems, enabling it to fill a niche…just as Genesis says? In Genesis 1:22 and 28, God said, "Be fruitful, and multiply, and fill" the earth. Before there was any death or survival, the Lord empowered His *creatures*, not His newly created environments, to perform the action of filling. Fulfilling His command would have required heritable adaptive programming in plants and animals right from the beginning.

   Adaptability is just a tool or stepping stone that enables the ultimate filling purpose. As traits are expressed in a population of organisms, some will "fit" better to different environmental conditions. This means they are physiologically more suitable and better able to extract resources. Organisms with those traits fill, pioneer, or move into that environment—they are not "selected for." The organism has the power and is active to either succeed or fail.

   Organisms express remarkable diversity of traits, at times quite rapidly—but always within the limits of their "kind" (Genesis 1:11-12, 21-25.) An *organism-based* paradigm is biblical. This explains how the process of organisms programmed to fit environments and fill them is the outworking of an intelligent plan, and not the product of an imaginary environment-based selector that "just happens."

Reference
1. Endler, J. 1992. Natural Selection: Current Usages. *Keywords in Evolutionary Biology*. Cambridge, MA: Harvard University Press, 220.

The Mind Behind the Design: Unraveling Life's Plans and Specifications

Questions

1. Skeptics ask how Christians can believe in immaterial things like God and angels when they cannot be quantified, measured, or weighed. Is there evidence for immaterial things?

_____

_____

_____

2. In what ways is DNA similar to a computer?

_____

_____

_____

3. What are the four key components of a specification, and why are they indicative of design?

_____

_____

_____

4. When you consider the whole concept of specification, why is the notion of "natural selection" important to evolutionists as a seemingly rational explanation for the origin of living things?

_____

_____

_____

Answers

1. Thinking itself and the transfer of those thoughts are immaterial. The thoughts that are being brought into existence right now contemplating evidence for immaterial things cannot be measured in any known way, even though activity in the brain as it thinks can be located and associated with various types of exposures. The thought is the framework, so to speak, directing brain activity as it tries to make associations, recall data, manage perceptions, and many other similarly complex activities. As far as is currently known to science, a thought has never been measured in terms of mass or energy…in other words, everyone's thoughts are immaterial, but very real.[1]

2. The molecule of DNA actually is the long-term storage, transferal, and recall center of the information for building a living thing. So it functions very similarly to the hard drive on a computer. Programs are stored on a hard drive and they also access the information off of a hard drive. The functions inside of cells are carried out by accessing information stored in the DNA. And just like a computer program needs an intelligent programmer, it is most reasonable to conclude that the incredibly complex code carried by DNA also had a programmer.

3. The key features of a specification are: 1) selecting 2) in advance 3) exact attributes 4) for a purpose. Intelligent behavior is recognized by the act of freely choosing from among several options for a purpose. From an experimental standpoint, only intelligent creatures (or man-made things) have ever been observed to make choices. So it would be scientifically inconsistent to apply any explanation other than an intelligent cause for the origination of the specification of DNA.

4. Engineers demonstrate intelligence in their design efforts primarily by selecting specific parts or processes and restricting others. The evolutionary story relies on ascribing an intention-to-act to the environment. From Darwin onward, evolutionists have extrapolated the idea that nature could make *choices*— which then allowed the seemingly plausible conclusion that nature actually does possess a sort of innate *intelligence*.

   Evolutionists downplay randomness and push the concept that natural selection constructs methodically—even claiming it behaves in law-like fashion. The connection is to know that selection, and its link to intelligent actions, is how Darwin successfully injected the attribute of intelligence into the non-living world.

Reference
1. An excellent resource for further information is Gitt, W., B. Compton, and J. Fernandez. 2011. *Without Excuse*. Atlanta, GA: Creation Book Publishers.

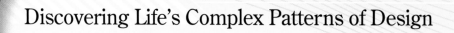

Discovering Life's Complex Patterns of Design

Questions

1. University of Chicago professor Jerry Coyne describes the evolutionary "retooling" of a shrew into a bat as a simple process. Why?

   _____

   _____

   _____

2. What is this article's definition for biological complexity? How could this be shortened even further?

   _____

   _____

   _____

3. How does this article's definition of biological complexity differ from the Intelligent Design definition?

   _____

   _____

   _____

4. If the probability of an event happening is astronomically low, do evolutionists approach the subject in the same way that scientists approach other subject areas? Why do evolutionists assert that gradual incremental biological change of one creature into a fundamentally different creature is reasonable when the probability is mathematically below the threshold of "possible"?

   _____

   _____

   _____

Answers

1. Dr. Coyne's description was a type of "shorthand" to represent all of the long, complex, and necessary steps evolution would need to get bat wings from shrew forelegs. Many evolutionists are certain that bats evolved from shrews, even though there is no fossil or observational evidence that any creature has ever changed into a fundamentally different kind. Thus, their use of the shorthand is invalid since it is said to represent evidence that does not really exist.

   If evolutionists listed the dozens of changes necessary to transform shrew forelegs into bat wings, people would be skeptical that it could happen. So calling the transition "simple" is more effective. Simple changes made to simple things are much more easily believed by people.

2. Biologically complex entities demonstrate many intricately arranged elements (parts or multi-step processes) functionally interconnected to satisfy an intended purpose. You could just say, "Biological complexity is numerous interconnected parts functioning together for a purpose."

3. There really is no difference. Intelligent Design researchers use a mathematical expression to describe numerous parts functioning together for a purpose. They define complexity in a statistical way that looks at the probability of getting a specified arrangement of specified parts. As long as an arrangement is specified, then probability—or the mathematical expression—is a legitimate way to look at complexity.

   Some people are more persuaded when they hear about numbers and probabilities, but you don't need calculations or mathematics to discuss either biological or man-made complexity. Most people intuitively know when they watch a car engine run that the probability of randomly getting all of those parts functioning together for a purpose is extraordinarily low. The probability argument is driven even deeper if they are asked to identify where natural forces alone have produced even two interconnected parts.

   So, stressing numerous interconnected parts functioning together for a purpose is the same mathematical probability argument, just expressed in a different—more intuitive—way.

4. Even though scientists have specific thresholds of probability where chance is eliminated from consideration as a possible explanation, evolutionists, in general, have no threshold. It is not uncommon for an evolutionist to say something like, "Well, the chance of that evolving is very low…but there's still a chance." At that point, wanting to "believe" in evolution has eclipsed the rational basis of seeing evolution as a scientific explanation for life's diversity because scientific evidence supports it.

   Another frequent response is, "Well, given enough time, there's a chance it could happen." This offers a totally unscientific evolutionary ploy of overcoming exceedingly low probabilities by imagining an essentially infinite number of chances occurring over unfathomable lengths of time. The goal is to get people to believe in evolution rather than show them that it has actually happened.

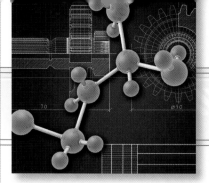

Life's Indispensable Microscopic Machines

Questions

1. Suppose in a lecture on how human engineers are increasingly copying the designs found in nature (an emerging field called biomimicry), you heard the speaker say, "Understanding and harnessing such phenomenal biological systems provides a strong incentive to design active nanostructures that can operate as molecular machines…[and] it should not be forgotten that nature has had a 4.5 billion year head start."[1] During the question and answer period, what question(s) would you ask about this statement?

_____

_____

_____

2. What explanation do many evolutionists offer for the origination of these molecular machines? How valid is this explanation?

_____

_____

_____

3. Why is telling someone about molecular machines one good way to explain the design found in living things?

_____

_____

_____

Answers

1. One question could be: "You described these complicated multi-part machines as part of 'phenomenal biological systems.' In all of human experience, when we see multiple parts functioning together for a purpose, *and their origination is known*, it is always due to an intelligent cause. You ascribe credit for the origination of these systems to 'nature' rather than to some intelligent cause, but isn't it more consistent scientifically to reason from what is known as far as a cause, to what is not known? Or do you exclude from the outset the explanation that it is due to an intelligent cause?"

   Since the lecturer has no experimental verification of any step-wise path leading to the development of these machines—and nor can he support by experiments that there has been enough time, even at 4.5 billion years—or of resources in nature that could produce these machines, his assertion of their totally natural origination is based on belief rather than science. The more that is known about these phenomenal systems, the more difficult it is to ascribe a plausible explanation that excludes intelligence and appeals only to nature.

2. Most evolutionary researchers would claim that these molecular machines were cobbled together from parts of other machines that were repurposed for new uses. However, a real Darwinian pathway must advance by "numerous, successive, slight modifications" (Darwin's words) due to random genetic mutations that are blind to any goal. Repurposing a pre-existing and functional machine into a new machine with a new purpose via the Darwinian path is *extraordinarily unlikely*, not to mention cobbling together a completely new system that cannot function until all of its parts exist and are in their proper place.

3. Most of life at the cellular level depends on operations by microscopic machines. People generally understand how machines work and actually find learning about them enjoyable. But the best reason is that since many cellular machines are very similar to human-designed machines—only far better—people will intuitively make the connection to design. You can be sure that even most scientists make the connection between molecular machines and human-designed things, as summarized by this molecular biologist:

   > It is notable that when describing the fruits of that work, those of us who work on cell signaling would be hard-pressed to avoid terms such as "machinery" and "mechanism." The analogy between cell signaling and man-made machines is all-pervasive, frequently adopting the imagery of elaborate clockwork mechanisms or electronic circuit boards. This perception is undoubtedly shaped by what we know: the machines that we use in our everyday life and the ways that we describe such machines in diagrams or in words.[2]

References
1. Browne, W. and B. Feringa. 2006. Making molecular machines work. *Nature Nanotechnology.* 1 (1): 25-35.
2. Mayer, B. J., M. L. Blinov and L. M. Loew. 2009. Molecular machines or pleiomorphic ensembles: signaling complexes revisited. *Journal of Biology.* 8: 81.

All-or-Nothing Unity

Questions

1. People can live with damaged or lost body parts. However, some parts are "vital." Name a few vital body parts.

_____

_____

_____

2. In construction projects such as building a road, a barn, or a skyscraper, many parts of the process must work together. What does it mean for a project to end properly, and how does the concept of all-or-nothing unity fit into that good outcome?

_____

_____

_____

3. Why is all-or-nothing unity such a powerful evidence for design?

_____

_____

_____

Answers

1. Heart, brain, a lung, a kidney, liver, a portion of some intestine, and skin (skin is an organ, though most people do not think of it as one). Everyone knows they can live without some body parts, but not their heart. But people may not know that hearts themselves have some vital parts that are made up of vital types of cells. This vitality continues all the way down to essential combinations of specifically shaped molecules—if any one of these in the chain is missing, the function of the heart ceases.

   "Life" is also defined as having several distinctive characteristics, including the ability to reproduce. Without all of the essential parts necessary for reproduction in both sexes, life would cease to continue for people.[1]

2. Most project managers would consider a project successful if it finished with high quality, on time, and within the amount of money allocated for it…and, of course, nobody was hurt. The quality issue is controlled with a quality control program and by each worker working according to certain standards and inspecting his/her own work. Another important tool is the schedule of work. If construction elements stay on schedule, the project should stay on schedule, which also helps control costs.

   In regard to all-or-nothing unity for construction, engineers must determine the phases of work that must be completed. Some tasks must have all of the parts and equipment available at the same place and right time for the task to be completed. Other phases and parts would be labeled as "critical," meaning a delay or failure to them would cause a delay and failure to the overall project.

   What does this have to do with living things? As biological researchers have discovered, the same types of functions controlling a construction project also seem to happen in living things. When something is made, like the duplication of DNA, there are resources that must be managed. So, it is not surprising that within cells there is information to manage quality control, such as molecules that "proofread" the newly copied sequence of DNA molecules. There is also a very precise schedule controlling things.

3. One reason why all-or-noting unity is good evidence for design is because it is very good evidence against evolution. The main mechanism of evolution, natural selection, is supposed to explain how things could look designed by intelligence even though they really were not. The key virtue of this explanation is that the origination of a huge amount of complexity does not need to be explained in one fell swoop, but in little steps at a time.

   Darwin stated that finding anything in biology that had to be explained by everything being in place all at once would amount to a miracle and would falsify his natural explanation. He said, "If it could be demonstrated that any complex organ existed which could not possibly have been formed by numerous, successive, slight modifications, my theory would absolutely break down."[2]

References
1. See Guliuzza, R. 2009. *Made in His Image: Examining the Complexities of the Human Body.* Dallas, TX: Institute for Creation Research.
2. Darwin, C. 1859. *On the origin of species by means of natural selection, or the preservation of favoured races in the struggle for life,* 6th ed. London: John Murray, 146.

Similar Features Show Design, Not Universal Common Descent

Questions

1. Imagine yourself as an evolutionist in the early 1960s after the discovery of DNA, the molecule of heredity, but before researchers had the ability to sequence the order of each nucleotide. How similar would you think the sequences of DNA are between a fruit fly and a human? Now suppose you were a creationist living at the same time. How would your predictions of sequence similarity differ?

_____

_____

_____

2. Evolutionists tailor their explanations to fit the surprising differences they find between creatures that are supposedly highly related. How do those explanations highlight the plastic-like attribute of evolutionary theory to absorb all observations—even those that are contradictory?

_____

_____

_____

Answers

1. Before technology existed to sequence each nucleotide of DNA, Harvard's leading evolutionary theorist predicted that looking for similar sequences of DNA between organisms would be pointless, since random changes over millions of years would obliterate any similarities—which, of course, he thought explained the differences in creatures.[1]

   The creationist model has always predicted that there would be similarities, even in DNA. The main things to explain are the differences between creatures. Designers know that many big changes in a final product can be effected with a few (much smaller) changes in the plans. Design-centered thinking is the key to understanding, and predicting, how DNA would control development.

   So it was not shocking news to creationists when recent DNA sequence analysis showed that human and fly had a roughly 70 percent commonality in genes. But this was a big surprise to evolutionists.[2] Many scientists think that the power of a theory is its ability to make correct predictions about future scientific findings. The few evolutionists who have made such predictions have been spectacularly wrong.

2. One of the best features of the scientific method is that explanations are constantly updated as new information is found. Some theories that consistently fail predictions, especially by wide margins, should even be discarded.

   Evolutionists, however, *believe* an effect is true (that all life descended from a common ancestor), even when the cause they thought was behind it is found to be incorrect. When even contradictory causes can easily be swapped out as the explanation for an effect, the validity of the effect (such as common ancestry) must be seriously questioned. When evolutionists allow any explanation or observation to be swallowed by their theory, the theory is said to be "plastic," which is not a real characteristic of scientific theories. The plasticity of many parts of evolutionary theory is pervasive in reports of new biological findings.

References
1. Mayr, E. 1963. *Animal Species and Evolution.* Cambridge, MA: Harvard University Press, 609.
2. Wilson, J. Study of flies proves fruitful. University of California, Irvine news release, November 2010.

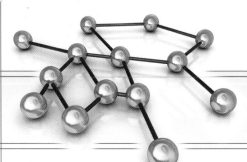

Similar Features Demonstrate Common Design

Questions

1. Creationists have held for decades that similar features show design—not universal common ancestry. Since these claims were made long before there was a way to sequence the genes underlying the features, can you think of any areas in which this prediction might have accurately guided research? (Hint: Think about how architects might use a previous set of plans for a three-bedroom house when they are given a contract to design a new four-bedroom house.)

_____

_____

_____

2. What is the general purpose for a creature's traits?

_____

_____

_____

Answers

1. One aspect of developmental biology is how multicellular organisms are built from a single cell. Creationist literature predicted that if the Intelligent Designer wanted an eye or an arm on different creatures, it would be reasonable to start with a basic set of plans for each of them. Evolutionists, on the other hand, argued that their substitute designer—natural selection—would find a way to evolve the features multiple times. The discovery of certain major genes called homeobox genes have seemed to confirm the creationists' explanation.

   An evolutionary developmental biologist describes the findings and their implications to the still dominant natural selection-based understanding of evolution:

   > When the sequence of these homeoboxes were examined in detail, the similarities among species were astounding. Over the 60 amino acids of the homeodomain, some mice and frog proteins were identical to the fly sequences at up to 59 out of 60 positions. Such sequence similarity was just stunning. The evolutionary lines that led to flies and mice diverged more than 500 million years ago, before the famous Cambrian Explosion that gave rise to most animal types. No biologist had even the foggiest notion that such similarities could exist between genes of such different animals…The story of *Pax-6* [the name given to a homeobox gene] suggests that the many types of animal eyes all took at least the *Pax-6* road. Natural selection has not forged many eyes completely from scratch; there is a common genetic ingredient to making each eye type, as well as to the many types of appendages, hearts, etc.[1]

   It seems that in this case the creationist prediction was correct and could have accurately focused research to look for a genetic basis for common design. The argument that similar features are based on a common design has been confirmed more strongly than ever with the newer understanding of the genetics underlying developmental biology.

2. It is a creature's traits that interface with environmental exposure. Exposures usually pose challenges to a population of creatures, especially if they involve extremes of rapid change. A creature's traits may continually solve the problem of new exposures in new environments and eventually enable all different kinds of creatures to *fill the earth* (see Genesis 1:22, 28; 8:17; 9:1, 7).

Reference
1. Carroll, S. 2005. *Endless Forms Most Beautiful.* New York: W. W. Norton & Company, 64, 72.

The Folly of Design without Purpose

Questions

1. In 1995, the National Association of Biology Teachers published a statement on the teaching of evolution that said, "The diversity of life on earth is the outcome of evolution: an unsupervised, impersonal, unpredictable, and natural process of temporal descent with genetic modification that is affected by natural selection, chance, historical contingencies and changing environments."[1] On December 21, 1997, *The New York Times* reported that the Association deleted some offending words in the statement after considerable debate and several votes.[2] In light of the article on how "purpose" relates to design, which words do you think were eliminated, and why were they removed?

   _____

   _____

   _____

2. Why are purpose and design inseparable?

   _____

   _____

   _____

3. Most evolutionists claim that the evolution of molecules and organs occurred by "natural selection" without a purpose. But that would seem to imply that human life has no purpose. Do some evolutionists claim that even the universe has no purpose? Could this lead to foolish explanations of human behaviors?

   _____

   _____

   _____

Answers

1. The National Association of Biology Teachers has changed their statement many times, and the current statement (see nabt.org) is very different from the 1995 one. The words eliminated from the earlier statement were "unsupervised" and "impersonal." Since purpose is tied to intelligence and volition, an impersonal, unsupervised process would not have purpose.

The reason the words were dropped is that there is no way to test for them and rule them out. They are more of a statement of belief and not something that could be backed up by scientific evidence. Although evolutionists can be very convinced that their substitute god, natural selection, explains design without God, they may not even realize when they have slipped into religious-like speculations that have no basis in science. For example: "All of this apparent design has come about without a designer. No purpose, no goals, no blueprints. Natural selection is simply about genes replicating themselves down the generations. Genes that build bodies that do what's needed—seeing, running, digesting, mating—get replicated; and those that don't, don't."[3]

2. Human actions are based on intelligence, whether conscious or unconscious. Unconscious activities even have an intelligent program underlying them, though there is a debate about the source of that intelligence (whether by totally natural processes or something that cannot be explained totally naturally). If you were to ask someone before they commenced an action *why* they were going to do it and they said that they "were not going to do it for any purpose," you could immediately see that "purpose" was included in their answer.

3. Some evolutionists are very candid about the fact that their worldview would lead someone to conclude that life really has no purpose. Consider the conclusion of evolutionist Richard Dawkins: "The universe we observe has precisely the properties we should expect if there is, at bottom, no design, no purpose, no evil and no good, nothing but blind, pitiless indifference."[4] It is a safe to say that if Dr. Dawkins were asked what experiments he had done and what scientific journal they had been published in which showed that throughout the universe there was "no purpose, no evil" and so on, there would be no direct answer to that question. His conclusion is a religious conjecture.

Michael Shermer tries to apply non-purposeful, evolution-based explanations even to human behavior. For example, Mr. Shermer wrote an article essentially denying sinful human behavior as a cause for the mutiny on the *HMS Bounty* and explaining the "ultimate" reason from an evolutionary perspective. He said, in part:

> A skeptic's explanation may seem less romantic, but it is more intellectually satisfying because it is extrapolated from scientific evidence and reasoning. There are, in fact, two levels of causality to consider: proximate (immediate historical events) and ultimate (deeper evolutionary motives). Both played a role in the *Bounty* debacle…Indeed, crews consisted of young men in the prime of sexual life, shaped by evolution to bond in serial monogamy with women of reproductive age….Proximate causes of mutiny may have been alcohol and anger, but the ultimate reason was evolutionarily adaptive emotions expressed nonadaptively, with irreversible consequences.[5]

References
1. NABT Unveils New Statement on Teaching Evolution. *The American Biology Teacher.* January 1996, 58 (1): 61-2.
2. Goodstein, L. Christians and Scientists; New Light for Creationism. *The New York Times*, December 21, 1997.
3. Cronin, H. 1998. The Evolution of Evolution. *Time, Special Issue: The New Age of Discovery*, 80.
4. Dawkins, R. 1995. *River Out of Eden.* New York: Basic Books, 133.
5. Shermer, M. A. Bounty of Science. *Scientific American*, January 12, 2004.

Evaluating Real vs. Apparent Design

Questions

1. The article used the word "better" over a dozen times to describe the comparison of scientific creationism to evolutionism. Why is it better for creationists to say "the creationist model of biological phenomena offers a better explanation of observations or data than evolutionism" than to say "science has proved creation" or "science has proved the Bible"?

2. Some evolutionists claim that biology is fundamentally flawed because biologists continue to write scientific papers with the words "purpose" or "design" or other synonyms when they "know" life on earth was not designed for a purpose.[1] Why is the use of those words a problem for evolutionists?

3. The article said the creationist model allowed researchers to escape a blinding mindset inclined to label findings as "junk," such as the hasty labeling of non-protein-coding DNA as "junk DNA." Some evolutionists say that problems like this are not serious, since science is self-correcting and mistakes are eventually found and amended. How would you respond to this, keeping in mind that many evolutionists claim their explanations disprove the observations that life was intelligently designed?

Answers

1. The Bible is self-authenticating, since it was written by the omniscient, omnipotent Creator, and is, by definition, infallible and true. However, human activities are incredibly far from being infallible. Creationists know many details of creation because of the revelation of the One who was there. But *proving* those facts—in other words, knowing and answering all of the possible arguments against them, within human limitations—is not possible. Humans implement science, and that inherently limits any claims about

science as having proved the Bible. In a way, there is also an undercurrent of arrogance when someone presumes that humans are capable of actually assessing the profound truths of the Bible against science and judging in the Bible's favor. It is more precise scientifically and theologically to say that the current findings of science *confirm* the biblical account of creation.

2. The criticism of some evolutionists is that their colleagues cause a problem just by using the word "design" to describe biological phenomena. For example, a paper by Timothy Bradley in *Nature* evidently stated insect respiration was "designed to function most efficiently." *The Scientist* said, "Bradley concedes that in his paper the word design is subject to misinterpretation, and he says that 'there is no reason for sloppy language'….[Brown University's Ken] Miller, who is also the coauthor of a widely used biology textbook, wouldn't use the word design with his students. 'They are going to take the language too literally, and it will cause a misunderstanding.'"[2]

   These evolutionists consider that since there is no designer, using the word "design" is fundamentally illegitimate—in spite of qualifiers like "apparent" or "illusion of" preceding it. It is also self-defeating from a strategic point. Why would any evolutionist persist in using "design," since that word by necessity evokes thoughts of a "designer" and will always be misinterpreted?

3. It is true that, in general, science is self-correcting. However, mistakes found in evolutionary biologists' assertions that certain findings invalidate intelligent design are often not corrected. Corrected findings and conclusions may be republished, but *not* the original claims regarding their now-mistaken implications against intelligent design. And the corrected original findings and conclusions usually do not generate nearly as much attention as the original reports.

   The problem is that it is the whole evolutionary paradigm—which expects to find "junk"—that is leading to the mistaken conclusions in the first place. These conclusions divert scientists' attention from asking the right questions. Many evolutionary biologists early on said that the hunt for function in much of the genome was a waste of time, since it was viewed as a hodgepodge of borrowed, copied, mutated, and discarded sequences. In 1980, Francis Crick, the co-discoverer of the structure of DNA, claimed that DNA whose function was not readily apparent "can be compared to the spread of a not-too-harmful parasite within its host…[and] it would be folly in such cases to hunt obsessively for one."[3]

   Such assumptions by Crick and others have been demonstrated to be spectacularly wrong. Unfortunately, their opinions were published in high school and college textbooks and popular science books that have not been corrected.[4]

References
1. Hanke, D. 2004. Teleology: The explanation that bedevils biology. In *Explanations: Styles of explanation in science.* J. Cornwell, ed. New York: Oxford University Press, 143-155.
2. Flores, G. 2005. Journals and intelligent design. *The Scientist.* 19 (4): 12.
3. Orgel, L. E. and F. H. C. Crick. 1980. Selfish DNA: the ultimate parasite. *Nature.* 284 (5757): 604-607.
4. An excellent and concise book on this subject written with lay readers in mind is *The Myth of Junk DNA* by molecular cell biologist Dr. Jonathan Wells, published in 2011 by Discovery Institute Press.

Life's Optimized Design Mirrors Its Perfect Creator

Questions

1. Evolutionist Richard Dawkins says that since the photoreceptors of the vertebrate eye point toward the back of the retina and the nerves face forward, supposedly "attenuating" some light, that this design would "offend any tidy-minded engineer!"[1] How would you respond?

   _____

   _____

2. Large robotic equipment is used in most automobile manufacturing. These robots are themselves built by other highly sophisticated robotic machines. Who made the robots? Would you find the answer "the robots did" satisfying?

   _____

   _____

3. What is the difference between an optimized design and an efficient design?

   _____

   _____

4. One way to understand the difficulty of optimization is to mentally design something. Human hands must balance a lot of competing design interests. Make a list of the needs vying against each other if you were to duplicate the human hand (for example, the need to be versatile and the need for ease of construction).

   _____

   _____

Answers

1. The argument that the eye is poorly designed is rarely made by: 1) people who really understand eye anatomy and function; 2) design engineers with experience putting together an optimum balanced design that incorporates several competing requirements; or 3) people who know the phenomenally complex biochemistry and physiology of the visual system.

   For example, the photoreceptors are highly metabolic and must be in contact with a layer called the retinal pigment epithelium in close approximation with another layer called the choroid. These layers are vital for the regeneration of the hyper-metabolic photoreceptors and removal of excess heat that would destroy the cells if they were not cooled.

From a pragmatic standpoint, there is no evidence that the layers of neurons obstruct light in any way. It can be demonstrated that the neurons in question are essentially transparent and have no appreciable effect on the photoreceptors' ability to detect light—of which the capability is down to a single photon, which is not possible to improve upon. A biophysicist who actually does research on the eye reported:

> The basic building blocks of human eyesight turn out to be practically perfect….Photorecep-tors operate at the outermost boundary allowed by the laws of physics, which means they are as good as they can be, period….Photoreceptors exemplify the principle of optimization, an idea, gaining ever wider traction among researchers, that certain key features of the natural world have been honed by evolution to the highest possible peaks of performance.[2]

Note that the phrase "honed by evolution" is magical, meaning it provides an explanation for origins, but leaps over all of the evidence necessary to back it up.

2. The answer might be considered satisfying because the question did not specify which robots were in mind. This illustration points up the problem of not asking the right question, or not asking a precisely word-ed question. Evolutionists exploit this problem all the time. For instance, living things have microscopic miniature machines that are necessary to manufacture all of the other machines. The information for the machines is specified in the DNA. Evolutionists always appeal to the information and machines *already existing* in the cell to explain the manufacture of DNA and cellular machines. This is cheating.

A better question would be, "Without referring to existing DNA or molecular machines, how do evolution-ists explain the *origination* of coded information in DNA and the complex protein machines that are neces-sary to manage the molecule?" Be prepared for the answer to swing wildly to a scientifically unsubstantiated story, as there are not any experimentally verifiable natural explanations for the origin of DNA and cellular machinery.

3. One word that is often substituted for optimum is "efficient." Efficient is not the same as optimal, but op-timized systems are generally very efficient. Efficient design is thoughtful use of resources to maximize the ratio of output to input of any system. This happens via the most effective use of resources to minimize wasting time, energy, effort, or expense. This adds yet another layer of difficulty to the design process.

4. Several important competing needs are: speed versus weight, strength versus weight, precision versus speed, and agility versus weight. The human hand balances these competing needs to a truly remarkable degree. Speaking about hand movements and the need for speed-versus-accuracy tradeoffs, researchers found: "Fi-nally, because our model intentionally uses idealized assumptions, its agreement with human data suggests that the biological system is controlled in a way that approaches the physical boundaries of performance."[3]

References
1. Dawkins, R. 1987. *The Blind Watchmaker*. New York: W. W. Norton and Co., 93.
2. Angier, N. Seeing the Natural World With a Physicist's Lens. *The New York Times*, November 1, 2010.
3. Venkadesan, M. and F. J. Valero-Cuevas. 2009. Effects of neuromuscular lags on controlling contact transitions. *Philosophical Transactions of the Royal Society A*. 367 (1891): 1163-1179.